A Letter From the Co-Founders of Secondary Entrance

Dear Customer,
We're delighted that you've purchased a Secondary Entrance practice pack! Before y ... ory of Secondary Entrance, and what our ethos is when it comes to providing education

As of June 2017, we had both been privately tutoring students for multiple years, a ... ed that we shared a few common frustrations. Firstly, we felt that existing practice ... on coaching exam technique rather than training aptitude. Secondly, materials in ... sly overpriced, and money was increasingly becoming a factor in academics. We also ... a child to work a limited number of hours in a day, and that it is therefore crucial to m ... Lo and behold, Secondary Entrance was born.

We set a goal: to develop affordable new resources of the highest quality. Together, we recruited the best minds from top universities in the world to create training tests for the four main pillars of secondary school admission: maths, English, verbal reasoning and non-verbal reasoning. Every question has been hand-crafted, debated over and scrutinised to ensure that it meets our exceptionally high standards. We ensured that the papers liberally use graphics to help develop children's visual and spatial skills alongside their intellect. In total, we've produced resources that give your child every chance of gaining admission to the school of their choice.

While our papers educate as well as monitor, we know that there is no substitute to having a good teacher. As such, we decided to compile a portfolio of tutors to offer both in-person and online tuition. We personally interviewed a wide range of candidates, selected the very best and trained them to Secondary Entrance quality. To complete our offerings, we've also uploaded a range of free resources on www.Independent11Plus.co.uk that we're constantly building on. Whatever it is that you need, we want to make sure that we've got you and your child covered. We'd like to wish your child all the best in their academic endeavours, not only for their upcoming exams but also for the journey that follows.

Warmest regards and happy testing,

Founders of Secondary Entrance
www.SecondaryEntrance.co.uk

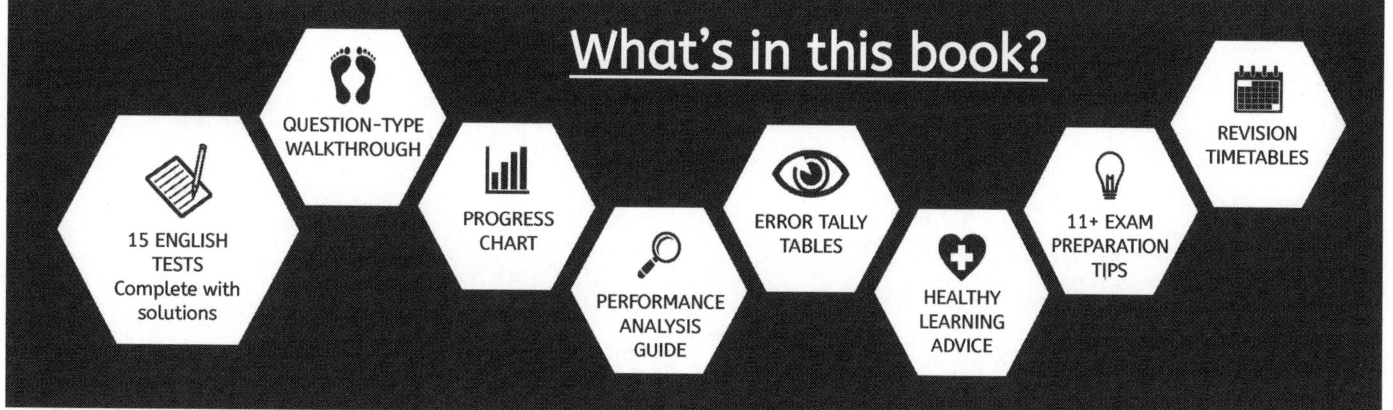

What makes these books so special?

There are three core aspects to what makes our papers unique, and which allow us to best support your child:

Quality

We offer the highest quality 11+ practice papers on the market, suitable for independent schools.

Diversity

We have 240 varied 11+ papers across four subjects, and our content is highly enriched with graphics and visuals.

Flexibility

Our papers get harder from Book 1 to 4 in each subject, and are all also highly effective for general aptitude training.

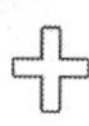

11+ Practice Papers
For Independent Schools & Aptitude Training

English

Book 1

Orders: Please contact www.How2Become.com

ISBN: 9781912370771

First published in 2020 by How2Become Ltd.

Disclaimer
Every effort has been made to ensure that the information contained within this resource is accurate at the time of publication. How2Become Ltd are not responsible for anyone failing any part of any assessment or selection process as a result of the information contained within this resource. How2Become Ltd and their authors cannot accept any responsibility for any errors or omissions within this resource, however caused. No responsibility for loss or damage occasioned by any person acting, or refraining from action, as a result of the material in this publication can be accepted by How2Become Ltd.

How2Become Ltd and its authors are not affiliated with any exam board, third-party service, or organisation and all guidance and advice provided is designed as an educational aid only.

The information within this resource does not represent the views of any third-party service or organisation.

As part of this resource, you are entitled to claim a 30-day free trial to our powerful online Independent 11+ Online Tuition Course...

GET FREE ACCESS NOW:

www.My11PlusCourse.co.uk

- ☑ 30+ Video Tuition Modules on Maths, English, Verbal Reasoning, and Non-Verbal Reasoning;
- ☑ 100s of interactive practice questions;
- ☑ Detailed answers to each question – ensure you can help your child learn how to pass each question type;
- ☑ Over 6 Hours of Tuition for Your Child;
- ☑ The only Independent School 11+ online tuition, practice, & mock-exam resource – from How2Become and Secondary Entrance;
- ☑ Try free for 30 days!

Contents

English - Syllabus Guide

Question types, advice and marking advice for the comprehension and writing tasks

Instructions for Usage:

> Run through this guide before attempting any of the papers.
> After completing tests, use this syllabus guide to find out weak topics.
> Use the writing task mark scheme to score essays.
> You can best document weak topics in the error tally table.

COMPREHENSION

Our comprehension exercises have been created using a variety of articles and texts, to expose your child to a truly broad range of possible material.

We believe that children should understand the context of language in a way it will be presented to them in real life, rather than just in an exam paper. Our English papers ultimately train your child to understand an article, critically break it down into its constituent parts, before then creating their own piece of writing in the form of a written task. This, we believe, is how English should be tested, and is the best form of training for all parts of what your child will be assessed on in an exam. From vocabulary, to understanding sentence structure, to learning spelling, everything will be assessed in each of our English papers. The comprehension and writing task contribute 20 marks each, making 40 marks in total.

What Articles Did We Use?

We have taken articles that are written in a number of different styles, including:

Book Excerpts

- These are some of the most typical types of comprehension to expect in an exam, and generally come from fictional books. Our papers contain a number of excerpts from fictional books written for your child's age, and therefore are perfect for assessment. The style should be familiar to your child, as it would be similar to the books they study in school, although a few papers have been made more challenging, introducing new vocabulary to expose your child to a higher level of English, to prepare them for anything they may be challenged with.

Science Journals

- These test your child's ability to absorb unknown content, and unfamiliar words. This best tests how to understand the context of an article, how to unpick facts, and how to follow a logical progression of ideas.

Newspaper Articles

- These present a story, sometimes in a biased way, to a wide audience. Here the language is of a simple level, yet deducing between fact and opinion may be tricky, and requires a detailed understanding of the nuances of journalistic writing.

Blogs

- These are the least formal of the English language texts in our tests. They adopt a sometimes 'chatty' form but are nonetheless a vital part of the English language in current society. Understanding how to convey a message in a relatable, quick and efficient way is a skill your child will need to be well accustomed to.

Instruction-Based Texts

- Whilst these could take a number of different forms, generally they are recipes or instruction booklet excerpts. These articles will be the most rigorous with respect to specific details within texts, and therefore require a thorough read of the article before attempting the questions.

What Sort of Questions can you Expect?

Our comprehension exercises contain, in general, 3 styles of questions: grammatical analysis, text analysis, and opinion-based questions.

Grammatical Analysis Question

- Each of our papers will contain at least 2 questions testing your child's understanding of the grammar within the text. This could be about specific words, such as finding an adjective, noun, verb or synonym. They could ask you to define certain unfamiliar words using the information provided to you. They may question your understanding of sentence syntax, such as why the author used direct text, or ended the story with an exclamation.

Sample Question: "Considering the text, suggest a synonym for the word 'unravel' (line 5). (1)"

NB: All questions end with a number in brackets indicating the number of marks available for this questions. They add up to a total of 20.

Text Analysis Question

- These questions are based directly from the text, asking you to recall facts from specific lines, and may ask for multiple points in order to obtain full marks. These questions could be in the 'true or false' style, or may ask you to rewrite parts of the passage. They assess understanding, and differentiate between students who have grasped just some concepts of the text, compared to those who have internalised everything including the abstract concepts.

Sample Question: "Using information in the text, state whether the following image descriptions would be more characteristic of a 1970s textbook or of a 2005 textbook, giving a reason for your answer in each case:

a) American fighter plane fires at Vietnamese soldiers. (2)

b) American soldier being treated in a hospital bed for severe injuries. (2)"

Opinion-Based Question

- These questions test a much broader understanding of the text. The overall aim is for students to fully take in the information in the text, and then use it to formulate concise arguments for questions posed towards them. These questions are therefore the most challenging, but also give very effective practice to your child. By forcing children to question why they believe certain ideas within a text, they'll begin to develop a foundation of critical analysis, and a fundamental basis for answering comprehension at all levels, even through to GCSEs.

Sample Question: "Re-read lines 1-11. How do you think Bob feels here? Use quotations to support your answer. (4)"

Written Mark-Schemes with Full Exemplar Answers

Each and every question has been planned and tested thoroughly to ensure it trains your child. Alongside a challenging set of questions, our papers offer unrivalled mark schemes, and offer further information, to reinforce learning. We want children to use our mark schemes to supplement their learning, and we want them to get the most out of every comprehension exercise.

Writing Tasks

To accompany our comprehensions, each English test has a writing task for your child, which varies in its nature. They form the final part of our all-encompassing syllabus, challenging your child to put to into practice all the language understanding they currently have, and to apply it to various situations. Each paper is accompanied with a full sample essay, written specifically to the title, and therefore provides a realistic idea of how your child could write their essay in the future.

<u>What Sort of Questions can you Expect?</u>

Our writing tasks fall into one of 5 categories:

Describing an Experience using Vivid Details

- For example, a title may be "You went scuba diving for the very first time at a coral reef. Write a diary entry describing what you experienced. (20)" This type of question looks at assessing the use of appropriate and extensive vocabulary to ultimately paint a picture in the mind of the reader. Furthermore, conveying this image effectively in a tone suitable for the setting is important. In order to achieve the top marks, there must be adequate sentence flow to ensure that the reader can follow a logical storyline.

Picture Description / Inspiration

- Some of our writing tasks will involve a picture, and asking the student to use it to create their own piece of writing. This style of question is very open, and encourages children to be creative, and to interpret the image in any way they like. Rather than looking for a detailed description of what the image contains, this question looks more for a story, with the image being just a snapshot of it.

Book Review

- This question type is rare, but is offered as a means of assessing your child's ability to summarise a piece of writing. This question will normally ask your child to analyse a book that they have recently read, and encourages the development of ideas and opinions.

Arguments For and Against a Case

- This is another less common question type. It asks your child to form arguments for and against a posed question, such as, "Should it be compulsory for every student to play a musical instrument?" This again develops a reasoning-based mindset for your child, getting them to think analytically about scenarios. It helps them with debating skills, including weighing up pros and cons in arguments.

Creative Writing

- This type of question encompasses the vast majority of writing questions your child might encounter. It assesses all of the following question types above: the ability to describe events vividly, to tell a story effectively, to develop ideas and opinions and to potentially develop arguments too. However, ultimately, the test of a good story is its effect on the reader - how much it entertains them. Whilst this may initially seem like a huge challenge, we have over 60 fully written exemplar answers, customised to each writing task of each English paper, to help get your child in the mindset of a budding author!

<u>How we Recommend that you Mark the Essays</u>

Overall mark: Out of 20

Planning (out of 3)
<u>3/3:</u> Planning is evident, well-structured and detailed OR the written response is very well-organised, follows a logical order and flows well.
<u>2/3:</u> An adequate amount of planning is present and some areas are detailed OR the written response is reasonably organised and follows a good order.
<u>1/3:</u> Minimal planning is present with no detailed areas OR the written response is not well organised or ordered.
<u>0/3:</u> No planning is present OR the written response shows no logical order, does not flow and is hard to understand.

Spelling and Grammar (out of 5)
<u>5/5:</u> At most, 2 grammatical or spelling mistakes across the entire response. Handwriting is neat and content is very clearly legible.
<u>3-4/5:</u> At most, 5 different grammatical or spelling mistakes across the entire response. Handwriting is acceptable, but could do with some improvement.
<u>1-2/5:</u> At most, 10 different grammatical or spelling mistakes across the entire response. Handwriting is not legible in areas and in other areas is untidy.
<u>0/5:</u> Significant grammatical and spelling mistakes throughout the entire response. Handwriting is not legible, and needs immediate attention.

Structure (out of 3)
<u>3/3:</u> Response is well-structured with sensibly sized paragraphs that logically compartmentalise the content.
<u>2/3:</u> Response has acceptable structure, but paragraphs may occasionally be used inappropriately.
<u>1/3:</u> Response has minimal paragraphing and poor structure. Content often appears to be in a big block and is difficult to read.
<u>0/3:</u> No paragraphing or attempt to form a structure.

Language (out of 4)
<u>4/4:</u> Varied and diverse use of language. Use of literary techniques such as tricolon, onomatopoeia, alliteration etc. Language is always appropriate to the context.
<u>3/4:</u> Good use of language in most areas. Some use of literary techniques. Strong attempt to adapt the language to set the scene.
<u>2/4:</u> Acceptable use of language, although sometimes it seems forced to fit the context. Literary techniques are used in areas, although largely absent.
<u>1/4:</u> Language makes sense, but is otherwise relatively basic. The language often does not fit the scene. Literary techniques are not used intentionally.
<u>0/4:</u> Language is largely incomprehensible, and is otherwise basic. The response cannot be understood well.

Content / Story (out of 5)
<u>5/5:</u> The response involves highly interesting content that draws the reader in. There are multiple plot points, written in a style that captivates. The work is original, and may target the question in an unexpected, novel way.
<u>3-4/5:</u> The response is interesting and has exciting stages. There is at least one clear plot, and the response makes good sense. The work addresses the question entirely.
<u>1-2/5:</u> While it may have interesting points, the response is repetitive and is not overly exciting. The plot is either unclear, underdeveloped, or does not make good sense. The response may only address part of the question.
<u>0/5:</u> The response has no obvious plot points. The content may be copied from a known book or resource. The work does not make sense. The response does not target the question at all.

English - Walkthrough

Full sample test, complete with worked solutions and tips

Instructions for Usage:

> Run through this guide before attempting any of the papers.
> Use this sample test to gain familiarity with this examination format.
> Attempt all of the questions, then review the worked solutions given.
> Refer back to this walkthrough when revisiting advice on exam technique.

Comprehension

Carefully read the passage below and answer ALL of the questions which follow.

The Interrogation: A short story

The door flew open and harsh artificial light flooded the tiny room. Bob squinted, attempting to defend himself from the accursed light and struggling to make out who, or what, had assaulted his senses. Two amorphous masses lingered in the brightly lit threshold for a second, then entered the room and locked the door behind them. 1

Fear and uncertainty gripped Bob. As the shapes drew closer, he realised that he was not going to enjoy what was coming. He attempted to stand up, to meet the black shapes head-on, but the closer of the two forms shoved him violently back into his chair. 5

Now Bob got a good look at the first intruder. The dark blob materialised into a tall, bulky man, his thick-rim glasses clinging to his head like moss to a cliffside. His angry grey eyes bore holes into the timid office worker's skull. Stomping around the desk toward Bob, he spoke, his voice imbued with the bass of a rockslide and the pride of a lion.

"What is the problem?" 10

Bob didn't understand. What was this idiot going on about? "I don't know what you are talking..."

The motion was so quick that Bob didn't even have time to comprehend what was about to happen. One moment, the bulky man had been standing completely still, and the next Bob's left cheek was stinging, red from the vicious slap that had been applied. The office worker was stunned. Had the goon even moved?

The man spoke again. "What is the *problem*?" 15

"Ow! What the hell was that for? I swear, I don't know what's going on!"

The second shape that had entered the room now calmly slid forward, materialising into a rail-thin woman with shoulder-length red hair flecked with blond streaks. She calmly strode to the opposite side of the desk from the brute and sat primly on the corner of it, right hand smoothing out the creases of her skirt as she did so, her left arm clutching a yellow notepad to her chest. Bob had to turn his chair in order to see her, but she did not turn toward him, her hair obscuring her face. 20

Then, after what seemed like ages, she spoke, her voice a melodious whisper: "Look, Bob, you're a nice guy, but we can't do our job without you telling us what exactly the problem is, okay? So just help us out, and we can let you go."

"Let me go? This is MY office!"

The redhead slowly nodded, then turned to look at the person whose office they had invaded. Her rich green eyes, too dark and vivid to be natural, found their purchase and burned themselves into Bob's memory. "Oh, we know. And yet, we can't let you leave, not until you give us what we want. We're on a *schedule* here, Bob, and you're holding us up. We need you to tell us what the problem is. Otherwise we can't do our jobs." 25

Bob was incensed. "Clearly you guys don't listen well. I already told you: I have no idea what you are talking about."

The woman's expression hardened, her silvery voice adopting a slight but noticeable edge. "My partner has already asked you once, and quite politely. Please don't make him repeat himself." 30

Bob stole a glance at the man, who was now towering over him from across the desk, and desperately racked his mind for something, anything, he could tell these two goons to make them leave him alone. He came up blank. "What, about the problem? What problem?"

The man stepped forward, as if to strike Bob again, but the woman held up her hand and he stopped. She sighed, and gracefully stood next to the corner of the desk. Even though when standing she was several inches shorter than he, at the moment, while sitting in his chair, Bob felt dwarfed by her presence. 35 37

Written by Matthew P Jones for Exception Not Found / CC 4.0
(https://www.exceptionnotfound.net/the-interrogation-a-short-story/)

END OF ARTICLE. Please answer the following questions:

Sample Question 1: Bob "squinted" in line 1. Why did he do this? (2)

Exemplar Answer: Bob squinted because the 'door flew open and harsh artificial light flooded the tiny room.' (1) By 'harsh artificial light' the author means that the room all of a sudden would be too bright and so Bob squinted to 'defend himself from the accursed light.' (1)

Tips: The first question will often be an easy one, and so in many cases the answer will be clear. If you do not know what the word means, then your best bet is to search for clues in the text! Bob's action of squinting follows the statement that 'harsh artificial light flooded the tiny room', and so we can assume that the squinting is a response to this light. In other cases, we can use other language clues to point us in the correct direction - for example, the word may be given as part of a list, and we can think about what kind of word would fit into this list. Sometimes the word may sound like the action which it conveys (eg. whooshing, whirring, sizzling) and this can be used to figure out the context in which it is being used. Always look at the number of marks on offer before you move on to the next question. Here there are two, with the second being for explaining why the brightness causes him to squint. Even if something seems obvious and well explained, you should write it down as there may well be an easy mark up for you to grab!

Sample Question 2: Which of the following words is least similar in meaning to "gracefully" (line 36)? (1)

a) Elegantly

b) Stylishly

c) Technically

d) Delicately

Exemplar Answer: c) Technically. (1) 'Elegantly', 'stylishly' and 'delicately' are all synonyms of 'gracefully', as each of these words indicates beauty of form in performance.

Tips: When attempting a question like this, make sure that you look at each and every option before settling on an answer. Doing so here may prevent you from making the mistake of missing 'least similar' and instead picking a word that is 'similar', of which there are three. If you are stuck, a good trick is to try and replace the word in the text with each of the options (in your head), and see which changes the meaning of the text the most.

Sample Question 3: Comment on the use and effect of the word "assaulted" (line 2). (2)

Exemplar Answer: The word 'assaulted' is a vividly violent, highly negative word which is commonly used to refer to physical attack. (1) As such, the use of this word shocks the reader and helps us understand how striking and startling this light was, counteracting typical initial assumptions of light being harmless. (1)
(1 mark for any analysis of the word 'assaulted' which supports a negative tone. 1 mark for an appropriate comment on how this affects the reader. Max 2 marks in total.)

Tips: This question calls on your deep analytical skills. When analysing a word or a phrase, there are several questions you must ask yourself. Is the word/phrase positive language or negative language? Is it vivid or dull? Is it normally used in that context or is it a bit of an unusual choice? Has it been used before in the text, or have any of its synonyms been used? Does it fit into the theme of the passage? Does it contrast a word nearby it? Does it rhyme with a nearby word? Are the sentences in the text short or long, and what effect does this have? Is this word/phrase at a key turning point in the story? You can keep going...

On answering questions like this, we can break down what the word or phrase does. Here, the word 'assaulted' is highly negative language. It is vividly aggressive, it is out of place in this context as it normally refers to a fight, it fits in with similar nearby 'fighting' vocabulary such as the word 'struggling' and so fits in with how the passage is developing. It does not contrast or rhyme with any nearby words and the sentences are of normal length. Overall, there are several things different to normal which makes the reader anxious and wary, and sets the tone for what is about to come.

Sample Question 4: What do you think the word "primly" (line 19) means? (1)

Exemplar Answer: Given the woman being described as 'rail-thin,' acting 'calmly' and how this is evidently meant to contrast with 'the brute', we might assume that primly means any of the following: elegant, correct, proper, polite, formal etc. (1)
(Accept any word or statement that suggests behaviour in a trained, proper manner)

Tips: You may not have a clue what the word means - in fact this question is quite difficult and you would not be expected to know the definition. However, there are plenty of contextual clues to help you figure out what is meant. You should look at the nearby choice of descriptive words, whether the tone of the conversation is generally positive or negative, whether the pace is fast or slow and see what kind of environment the author is trying to create. Based on this, it should be possible to work out that the lady is being described as corporate, well-dressed and organised, and as such the suggestions above are consistent with the setting.

Sample Question 5: Re-read lines 7-9. Pick one simile and one metaphor from these lines and describe its effect. (4)

Exemplar Answer: Simile: 'thick-rim glasses clinging to his head like moss to a cliffside'. (1) The detailed imagery here allows us to picture just how firmly rooted the man's glasses were to his face, and makes them a part of his identity, since the reader can visualise how tightly attached moss is to rock. (1)
Metaphor: 'His angry grey eyes bore holes into the timid office worker's skull'. (1) This vivid imagery highlights how piercing and menacing the man's stare was, to have such an effect as to appear to drill holes into Bob's skull. (1) OR 'with the base of

a rockslide' (1) which again uses imagery of vast numbers of rocks tumbling to allow us to picture his rumbling sound being generated. (1) OR 'with the pride of a lion' (1) which uses the comparison of his voice to that of a strong, majestic animal to allow us to appreciate the strength in his speech. (1) Interestingly a group of lions is called 'a pride' and so the author may be using double-entendre (i.e. making a pun) to put even more character and strength into the man's voice. (1)
(1 mark for identifying the simile. 1 mark for appropriate corresponding analysis as to the effect that it has. 1 mark for identifying a metaphor. 1 mark for appropriate corresponding analysis as to the effect that it has. Max 4 marks in total.)

Tips: First of all, make sure that you know what a simile is and what metaphors are! A simile is when one thing is compared to another and therefore put into context - for example, 'as white as snow'. A metaphor is when a word or a phrase is used in a context where it is not literally applicable, in order to indicate similarity between the two ideas - for example, 'her eyes were sparkling diamonds'. Be careful as it is easy to confuse them - for instance, 'her eyes were as sparkly as diamonds' is a simile not a metaphor. When using similes or metaphors you can always comment on how they put the described thing into a real life context and help the reader better understand it, by drawing a comparison to objects or phenomena that the reader is more familiar with.

Sample Question 6: Re-read lines 19. How do you think Bob feels here? Use quotations to support your answer. (4)

Exemplar Answer: Bob was confused and disoriented, as he was 'struggling to make out who, or what had assaulted his senses'. (1) Bob was afraid, as he was gripped by 'fear and uncertainty'. (1) Bob felt as if he was in danger, shown when he was 'attempting to defend himself from the accursed light'. (1) This is further reinforced when Bob realised that 'he was not going to enjoy what was coming,' as he is full of dread as to what may be in store for him. (1) His fear is further evident by his vigilance - for example he is portrayed to be attempting to get 'a good look at the first intruder.' (1)
(1 mark for each description of how Bob may feel that is supported by a suitable quotation, adjective or piece of analysis of the text. Max 4 marks in total.)

Tips: When a question asks you to use quotations, you should assume that for each factual point you can earn 1 mark and for each supportive quotation you can earn 1 mark. In this context, you should never make a point without justifying it with information from the text. The question here makes you put yourself in the shoes of one of the characters, and you should immerse yourself fully into the story. Think how you would feel if you were in Bob's position. Try and identify exact adjectives or descriptions that describe the person's state - here these are 'fear and uncertainty' to pick up the easy marks. Beyond this, marks will be awarded for analysis of language - for instance the aggression in the word 'assaulted' and panic in the word 'struggling'. You can also pick up marks for analysing sentence structure - if you think that the sentences are particularly long or short, they can disrupt the flow of the text and add to the panic. If you are struggling to find things to say, a point that is often applicable at turning points in plots is that the language becomes more vivid to make the reader feel as if they are in the same environment as the character.

Sample Question 7: Re-read lines 12-14. Comment on the way this paragraph is written. How does it mimic Bob's own experience of the events which it describes? (3)

Exemplar Answer: These lines are written in an unusual way. They describe Bob's sensations before they describe the slap itself – we are only told about what has happened towards the end of the paragraph. (1) This means that at first the reader is confused as to what is happening, which is much like the confusion and startle that Bob would have been experiencing while this was occurring. (1) The author focuses on the timing and the stinging sensation on Bob's cheek when the reveal occurs (1) which draws attention to the power of the slap and the confusion it caused. (1) The use of short sentences at the end of the paragraph (1) further creates a tense, stunned atmosphere as it throws the reader off. (1) A rhetorical question is used at the very end (1) which conveys Bob's confusion by changing the tone to an inquisitive one. (1)
(Max 2 marks for commentary on the sentence structure, sentence order, choice of vocabulary or any other appropriate features of how this paragraph is written. Max 2 marks for appropriate corresponding analysis of how each mimics Bob's experience of the events. Max 3 marks in total.)

Tips: When you are specifically asked to comment on the writing style, you should make a system for how you analyse the text. Answer the following points in your order of choice: Are the sentences particularly long or short? Is the order of the text normal? Is the language used normal, or is it particularly positive, negative, colourful or dull? Does the author use rhetorical questions? Are there lots of unusual punctuation tools used? Is the paragraphing normal? Is there lots of conversation from characters? Does the language contrast the paragraphs before or after in any way? There are several more such questions which you should ask yourself, and keep a note of what is interesting. When you make your points for each of these, you must analyse what the aspect of the writing style that you have commented on actually does. For instance, if you state that the author uses lots of rhetorical questions all of a sudden, you must then go on to explain that this could demonstrate that the character is questioning a lot of things, and so could be confused.

Sample Question 8: What comparisons are made between the two intruders? Use quotations to illustrate your point. (4)

Exemplar Answer: Where one interrogator is described to 'stomp around the desk', the other is said to have 'calmly strode to the opposite side of the desk'. (1) The difference in language used to describe the way each character walks highlights differences in their attitude, with one being much more violent and the other being much more graceful. (1) The voice of the larger character was 'imbued with the bass of a rock slide and the pride of a lion', whereas that of the lady was 'a melodious whisper'. (1) Whereas the larger character is loud, the lady is made to seem as if her speech is a soft and quiet. (1) Other comparisons to be drawn could relate to build, a 'dark blob materialised into tall bulky man' compared to the 'rail-thin woman'. (1) Finally, the actions of the two characters varies in aggression, with 'the bulky man' who 'delivered a vicious slap' contrasting the gentle woman who 'was smoothing out the creases of her skirt'. (1)

(Max 2 marks for any valid comparisons made between the two intruders. Max 2 marks for appropriate corresponding quotations supporting these comparisons. Max 4 marks in total.)

Tips: The most common error on questions like this is not following the question directly. You should not write one paragraph about one intruder followed by another paragraph about the other - do not assume that the examiner knows what you are comparing. You must put the exact comparisons for each character side by side to earn each mark, and there is often 1 mark for quotations showing the comparisons, and 1 mark for the analysis of what is being compared. You should not hesitate to state the obvious - while one interrogator is seen to 'stomp around the desk' and the other is said to have 'calmly strode to the opposite side', you must directly state that one is moving aggressively and the other peacefully. Finally, you should remember that 'comparisons' can be differences or similarities, whereas 'contrasts' means that you are only searching for differences.

Writing Task

Sample Question: Create a piece of descriptive writing about an abandoned mansion, describing the mansion in detail. (20)

Exemplar Response:

The abandoned mansion loomed gloomily at the top of the hill. I had walked past it every day for almost two years on my way to school, but the boredom of these long summer months compelled me to finally visit it. I approached it tentatively, appreciating how it must have been truly majestic in its prime. Two cracked marble columns bordered the grand, mahogany door like a picture frame. I uncertainly placed my trembling palm on the large brass doorknob that was firmly embedded into the centre of the imposing door, and gave a strong push. The door gave way, revealing what lay behind it.

Ahead of me lay a grandiose, spiral staircase in the centre of the entrance hall. Ivy had entwined itself into the banister and delicate metal detailing on the staircase. I treaded softly along the cracked, grey marble floor that was probably once white. The rubber soles of my shoes made no noise as I negotiated the rubble strewn across the ground, tiptoeing quietly so as to not be heard. On either side of the high-ceilinged entrance hall were stained-glass windows; despite being covered in a thick blanket of dust, I could still appreciate the deep red, blue and green light that filtered through the glass.

I walked past the staircase rather than up it, due to the fact that many stairs had now been replaced by emptiness, and to go up would probably be too treacherous. Through a door on my left I saw what clearly used to be a cinema room. Two velvet curtains clung desperately to the ceiling on either side of the screen, and the maroon-coloured leather reclining chairs were full of wrinkles. I walked further on, and reached the kitchen. A kitchen island with a porcelain sink stood in the middle of what was obviously a family kitchen. Idyllic pictures of a family long forgotten occupied every spare space in the kitchen. The cupboards were fully stocked with glasses, plates, bowls and cutlery. The dining table was fully set, as if dinner was about to be served. The entire mansion appeared to be frozen in time, making me wonder what forced this family to leave their lavish home so suddenly. Walking past the abandoned mansion now no longer filled me with fear as it used to, but with a profound sadness.

Tips:

There are five core elements to ensuring that you produce a strong piece in the 11+: planning, timing, grammar, language and paragraphing.

Planning: It is important to shape your piece with a strong plan before you start writing - you should spend about 20% of your time on this stage. Plan with the intention of writing 3-4 paragraphs, and write down your core plot points, the plot twists that you may bring in, and work on a strong opening line. Ensure that you organise your writing well, as there is nothing worse than misinterpreting the brilliant things that you have already put to paper! Always hand your plan in along with your full written response, as often the examiners give credit for it, especially if you do not finish your piece.

Timing: One of the biggest errors that children sitting the 11+ make is spending too long on the opening paragraph and rushing through the rest without thought. While you should place a slight bias of time on the introduction and conclusion, since these are the first and last things respectively that the examiners read, you should by no means rush the middle as this contains the body of your response and holds most of the plot points.

Grammar: Quality, not quantity! It may be hard to believe, but it really is far more important that what you write is of the best quality that you can produce rather than being as much as possible. There are lots of points at stake for grammar, so make sure that you know how to use commas, colons, semi-colons, capital letters and punctuation marks, and be certain that you know how to introduce and close speech. If you are in doubt over using a particular grammatical tool in the actual exam, then you may well be best off simplifying your writing to avoid using it.

Language: It is important to use a diverse and colourful array of language in the 11+. Make sure that you touch up your vocabulary very regularly, and that you have a good understanding of interesting new words before you use them. Similes, metaphors, rhetorical questions, 'rules of three' and other linguistic tools look very good, so try and slip these into your writing if you are able to.

Paragraphing: This is surprisingly simple, yet so many candidates get it wrong! You should paragraph when: changing topic or introducing a new idea, putting opposing ideas next to each other for contrast, a character is beginning to speak, and if a paragraph is too long and you have found a sensible excuse to split it up. Typically the first and last paragraphs are 3-4 lines long, and the middle ones are 5-8 lines long. These rules are not hard-and-fast, you should adapt them around your plot, not the other way round. Remember to indent at the start of a new paragraph!

English - Tests 1-15

Time allowed for each paper : 70 minutes

Instructions for Best Practice:

> Attempt all of the questions.
> Aim to spend 40 mins on each Comprehension and 30 mins on each Writing Task.
> Write all of your responses on separate lined paper.
> Equipment recommended: 2 x Pencil, 1 x Eraser & 3 x A4 Lined Sheet.

Marks

Comprehension

Carefully read the passage below and answer ALL of the questions which follow.

Finding pottery in Provence

I have a particular fondness—a weakness, some friends say—for ceramics, and my cupboards are crammed with pieces that I've bought all around the world. Besides enjoying the quirky beauty of my fire-blackened Indonesian bowls, polka-dotted Hungarian wine jugs, and Tunisian pitchers with their otherworldly iconography, I take a perverse pleasure in the challenge of lugging pottery home from overseas. It's ridiculously breakable; each undamaged plate is a trophy. (lines 1–5)

My favourite finds, the ones I use every day, are from the south of France, where the history of this craft is long and cross-cultural, absorbing influences from throughout the Mediterranean. The region's earliest inhabitants made primitive vessels for storing, cooking, and serving food. The Greeks introduced more sophisticated techniques when they founded Marseilles as a trading port, circa 600 B.C. (They also introduced wine, an instant hit.) Trade with Italy and Spain brought new shapes and coloured glazes. When the popes settled in Avignon, in the early 1300s, they promulgated both religion and luxurious dining. (line 10)

Pottery making seems especially suited to the Gallic temperament. Like cheese and wine production, it's a blend of chemistry, artistry, geography, luck, and sweat. Southern France's terroir is ideal-clay-rich soil, hot sun for baking, wood for firing. Today, it has become inseparable from what we think of as the southern French style. Provençal cuisine conjures up the mortar and pestle, terra-cotta cookware, and brightly coloured olive-oil jugs and kitchen tiles. And the dishes and plates: even on the gloomiest winter day, the warm glazes and familiar rusticity evoke herb-scented Mediterranean sunshine. (line 15)

I've collected most of my pottery over the years on shopping expeditions with my friend Christopher Corr, the British illustrator; he has a centuries-old limestone maison in Barjac, about an hour's drive northwest of Avignon, on the border of Provence and the Languedoc. Christopher's kitchen cabinets groan under the weight of a collection that is bigger and more eclectic than mine—he has the advantage of proximity. (lines 20–21)

Written by Anonymous for Discover Uzes / CC 3.0
(http://www.discover-uzes.com/2010/03/finding-pottery-in-provence.html)

END OF ARTICLE. Please answer the following questions:

1) Name three countries that the writer owns pottery from. (3)

2) What do you understand of the words "otherworldly iconography" (line 4)? (2)

3) What is meant by the word "quirky" (line 2)? Suggest a word which means the opposite of "quirky". (2)

4) Which of the following is pottery not a mix of according to the article: (1)

   a) Chemistry
   b) Geography
   c) Patience
   d) Fortune
   e) Sweat

5) What three things make the South of France ideal for pottery? (3)

6) What is "the advantage of proximity" (line 21) in this context? (2)

7) Why do Christopher Corr's cabinets "groan" (line 20)? (2)

8) Using information from the text, determine whether the following statements are true, false or more information is needed to be sure.

   a) Avignon is southeast of Barjac. (1)
   b) Marseilles became a trading port roughly 1,400 before the 21st century. (1)
   c) The author has collected most of his pottery by online shopping. (1)
   d) The Greeks are the people most known for having introduced new shapes and colours to pottery. (1)
   e) Christopher Corr lives in Barjac. (1)

Writing Task

Pretend that you are an astronaut in a spacecraft orbiting the earth. Write a letter to your friend describing what it's like to be in space. (20)

Marks

Comprehension

Carefully read the passage below and answer ALL of the questions which follow.

What is Yoga?

Many of us have practised Yoga for years, yet if someone asks us for a definition of what Yoga is, we would be hard pressed to give an answer. As many other important products of ancient Indian culture, Yoga isn't clearly defined and systematised like the scientific disciplines of the West. In this article, I will try to give a personal contribution to this subject; it is not a clear, simple definition I'm looking for, but rather an unveiling of the essence of this amazing science. Let us start, then, with a classical definition of Yoga. 1 5

A classical definition of Yoga.

Sure enough, a clear, concise definition has been already given by a great sage: I am talking about Patañjali who, in his *Yoga Sutras*, presents the first written systematisation of the methodology and philosophical principles of Yoga – a discipline that had been existing for centuries before his birth. In Book 1, Sutra 2, we have one of the most famous definitions: 10

Yoga is the cessation of the fluctuations of the Mind.

For many commentators, this Sutra expresses the ultimate objective of Yoga: to tame the mind, stop its uncontrolled fluctuations, and focus it at will on an object of meditation. Other scholars of Patañjali propose a slightly different interpretation. For them, the Sutra 2 which I just quoted expresses the means, or the methodology of Yoga; the goal, instead, is explained in the next Sutra (Book 1, Sutra 3): 15

Then, the Seer can abide in its own Nature.

So, according to this view, by calming and focusing the mind, we can allow our inner Self, the Witness consciousness which is before and beyond the mind, to shine through, and abide in its own true condition. I personally interpret this Sutra as referring to a state of ultimate presence (very much like what Eckhart Tolle describes as "Now" in his inspiring book, "The Power of Now"), although others might have different opinions. 20

When reading a text like the *Yoga Sutras*, a certain degree of ambiguity is unavoidable. In ancient India, Sutras were written in an ultra-concise form, probably to make them easier to memorise and repeat orally with minimal changes. All non-essential words are omitted, and the words that are used are often charged with more than one deep meaning. Thus, in classic Yoga we don't often find the systematic, organised structure of physics, mathematics or other scientific disciplines, and interpretation is almost always possible. This is also related to the fact that Yoga, unlike mathematics, deals with sentient beings, who are by nature much harder to describe and categorise than, for example, chemical elements or geometric entities. 25

As a consequence, we do have a certain degree of freedom in talking about Yoga, its objectives and methods; a freedom we don't usually enjoy in more academic disciplines, where it's crucial to reach a universal consensus about definitions, and ambiguity is not well tolerated. Thus, nowadays there are many alternative, sometimes contradictory points of view on Yoga; however, this doesn't seem to be a big problem for practitioners, who are generally happy to follow their own path and quite tolerant of the others. Let's then have a quick look at some modern interpretations of Yoga. 30

Some modern definitions of Yoga.

Even though there aren't, in modern times, such a famous definition as Patañjali's, it's still possible to identify some general approaches to Yoga. Here is a short, incomplete list: 35

Yoga as Fitness.

Many students and teachers in the West, but also in India, stress the importance of the benefits of Yoga on physical health. Thus, the main focus is placed on the practice of *asanas* (postures), and on the perfection of alignment. The therapeutic effects of each posture are sometimes studied in depth, so that a personalised practice can be devised, in order to address specific health conditions. In other styles of Yoga, the emphasis is on a powerful, dynamic practice that acts more as a prevention than a cure: the student is constantly stimulating her energetic system and attaining a state of permanent physical balance and health. 40

Yoga as Meditation.

Another modern interpretation sees Yoga as primarily a meditation technique. Here, the focus is on calming and stabilising the mind, through the use of *asanas*, *pranayama* (breath control), as well as mental concentration techniques. Schools that follow this interpretation usually do not give so much importance to alignment in the postures, or to the physical benefits of Yoga; instead, the body is used as a tool to access one's own mind and gain more control over it. This view of Yoga is more in line with Patañjali's 45

Marks

definition, especially the one contained in Book 1, Sutra 2 ("Yoga is the cessation of the fluctuations of the mind"). 50

Yoga as Union.

Some practitioners and schools understand Yoga as a process of union between one's own internal world (sometimes called the "Microcosm") and the Universe (the "Macrocosm"), Nature, or God. Schools who follow this interpretation are very focused on *Bhakti* (devotional) practices, such as Mantra chanting, rituals, and so on. The practice of postures, breathing exercises, and other techniques is seen as a tool to facilitate the union, or dissolution, of the individual Self into a higher, superior entity. The positive consequences on health, as well as the mental concentration that can be attained through the practice of Yoga, are seen as secondary effects, although beneficial. 55

Yoga as Evolution. 60

Finally, I would like to contribute with a last personal definition of Yoga:

Yoga is a practical philosophical system whose objective is the physical, mental and spiritual evolution of the human being.

By practical philosophical system, I mean that Yoga is a (mostly) coherent, systematic discipline in which philosophical concepts and practical methodologies are inextricably linked. According to my understanding, the objective of Yoga can be defined as promoting the evolution of the practitioner. By evolution, I am referring to a process in which the connectedness and/or internal harmony of a being are increased (if this sounds a bit confusing, you can have a look at my article on Evolution). 65

Conclusion.

I believe that all these views of Yoga are valid as long as they don't claim to be the only "correct" stance. There is no reason to look for a complete, absolute definition of Yoga; as I have tried to express before, Indian philosophy is not obsessed with exactitude and precision, but instead happily accepts some degree of freedom and individual interpretation. In fact, most practitioners have a personal, unique conception of Yoga that contains some elements of each of the approaches we have mentioned here. 70

With this premise, I'd like to share my personal view of Yoga as a methodology to promote evolution in the human being. It's not the only path that leads to evolution, nor necessarily the most appropriate for everyone. Nevertheless, it is a beautiful system that has been practised and refined during centuries, and whose validity can be tested directly on oneself. It does not require any special skills or attitudes, except for patience, constancy, and a sincere aspiration to evolve. 75 79

Written by **Raffeallo Mancorda** for **Fragments of Evolution** / CC 3.0
(http://fragmentsofevolution.org/what-is-yoga/)

END OF ARTICLE. Please answer the following questions:

1) Why were the sutras written in 'ultra-concise form' (line 22)? (2)

2) What are the two possible interpretations of Patanjali's Yoga Sutras' definitions of Yoga, and in what way are they similar to one another? (3)

3) In what way is yoga less systematic than Western disciplines? (3)

4) Briefly summarise each of the four modern applications of Yoga, including what you feel are all the important points mentioned in the text (7)

5) Using information from the text, determine whether the following statements are true, false or more information is needed to be sure.

   a) People tend to follow one of the definitions exactly as it is; they make this their ideology. (1)
   b) Considering Yoga as Union: the health benefits which can be gained are not the primary goal of the practice. (1)
   c) According to the author, out of all of the possible views of Yoga there is one version which is considered to be right. (1)
   d) A small number of schools see Yoga as a union of the real world and heaven. (1)
   e) Considering Yoga as Evolution: Yoga is seen to be a non-methodical practice in which thoughts and actions can be split. (1)

Writing Task

Create a piece of descriptive writing about an animal, describing the animal in detail. (20)

Marks

Comprehension

Carefully read the passage below and answer ALL of the questions which follow.

What American textbooks say about Vietnam, and about Americans' attitudes toward war.

Textbooks are opportunities for governments to instil patriotic values in school children. Such values are especially important if a government wants its citizens to support future wars. Governments that seek to convince their soldiers to fight, kill and die in wars need to present past wars as glorious and honourable and minimize the wartime suffering of the country's soldiers. However, textbooks, deliberately or inadvertently, can also open space for 'critical pedagogy' that undercuts militarism by presenting the human costs of war for soldiers and civilians. 1 5

Textbooks are especially influential in shaping US students' opinions on war. This is because American high school teachers, unlike their counterparts in Europe and Asia, are not trained in history, having majored in education or social science disciplines, like sociology or psychology. Thus, the decisions made by U.S. textbook authors and publishers are decisive in determining what students learn about America's wars. 10

Publishers in the U.S., as elsewhere, want to sell as many books as possible and therefore seek to avoid offending the often-conservative state and local school boards that select textbooks. This leads to fairly bland volumes that say little about controversial topics like the Vietnam War, or that muddle any contentious message with multiple points of view. Nevertheless, even as publishers try to evade controversy, textbook authors, as they select words and images, make editorial choices that shape how students view specific wars and influence their stance toward the military and war in general. 15

The Vietnam War has been America's most contentious foreign war. It was the one war the United States unambiguously lost, and it provoked a level of domestic opposition greater than any other U.S. foreign war. For those reasons, textbook depictions of the Vietnam War provide a good insight into critical views of war, and shines the light on those who opposed a war while it was going on. 20

With a graduate student Lacy Mitchell, I examined U.S. high school social studies textbooks published between 1970 and 2009. I found that in the early 1970s, during the last years of the Vietnam War and its immediate aftermath, descriptions of the war were mainly impersonal and presented the actions of American soldiers in neutral terms.

For example, textbooks paid little attention to the experiences of individual American soldiers. Instead the chapters on Vietnam mention the numbers of casualties without evaluating the worth or costs of soldiers' sacrifices; accounts of battles such as the Gulf of Tonkin or Khe Sanh present events and outcomes without presenting soldiers' actions as either glorious or hellish. 25

In essence, textbooks showed American actors in Vietnam *as* the United States, or its armed forces as a collectivity rather than as individuals who fought in the wars. The dominance of this impersonal approach to Vietnam, and to the other U.S. wars discussed in textbooks, supports the view that textbooks offer a 'hidden curriculum' of militarism and nationalism. However, this approach has changed since the 1970s. 30

Decade by decade, the Vietnam War has been presented in increasingly negative terms. In our inventory of textbook items (paragraphs, photographs, student exercises) the percentage that presented the Vietnam War as glorious fell from 5% in 1970 to close to 0% in the 1990s, and it has remained at zero in subsequent decades. The share of items that present the war as hellish rose from 15% in 1970 to 33% in 2009. All the negative portrayals show the horror of the war through the personal experiences of American soldiers and focus on their deaths and suffering. 35

Photos of U.S. soldiers in Vietnam have also become increasingly graphic. In the 1960s and 1970s, photos show helicopters over Vietnamese terrain with no humans present and fully intact U.S. soldiers. Beginning in the 1980s, textbooks include more and more photos of booby traps designed to mangle the bodies of soldiers, bloody and bandaged soldiers, soldiers crying alone with captions describing their mourning of lost comrades, and disabled veterans. Soldiers are quoted directly describing their own suffering and trauma. 40

Marks

Vietnam also stands out from textbooks' approach to other American wars, in that coverage of the Vietnam Veterans' Memorial and veterans' issues became a key theme after the opening of the Memorial in 1982. Textbooks occasionally have photos of memorials for other wars but do not discuss them in the chapters on those wars. 45

It is important to emphasise that, despite these changes, U.S. textbooks still have almost nothing to say about the suffering and deaths of Vietnamese soldiers or civilians. Students who read U.S. textbooks can come away thinking that only Americans suffer in war. Similarly, Japanese textbooks ignore Japan's World War II atrocities while German textbooks give great attention to Nazi war crimes and genocide. Textbooks that mention the My Lai massacre (and that is the only reference to Vietnamese civilian deaths in most of the textbooks) present it as an isolated incident. The focus on Americans' pain also allows textbooks to avoid any discussion of American responsibility and guilt for the war. Anti-war protests are noted in the textbooks, but no attention is given to the content of the protesters' criticisms. 50 55

It may be that American textbooks' increasing focus on the suffering of individual soldiers in the Vietnam War is a reflection of a growing 'world culture' that values individual persons above the nation or governments. However, although it was present, we found much less focus on soldiers' suffering in textbook discussions of World War II, suggesting that the Vietnam coverage was in part a response to a unique military defeat. Nevertheless, the highly negative portrayal of Vietnam, and the increasing focus on American soldiers' suffering in other wars, reflect and may contribute to a growing intolerance, at least in the United States and other wealthy nations, towards casualties of a nation's own soldiers. 60 63

Written by **Richard Lachmann** for **World Education Blog** / CC 3.0 (https://gemreportunesco.wordpress.com/2017/01/11/what-american-textbooks-say-about-vietnam-and-about-americans-attitudes-toward-war/)

<u>END OF ARTICLE. Please answer the following questions:</u>

1) Why are history textbooks more influential in the US than in most other countries? (1)

2) Re-read lines 1-6. Why might a country's government want to influence the contents of its textbooks? Why is it important that it does this? (2)

3) Re-read lines 11-16. What is the main goal of publishing companies, and what effect does this have on the material that they publish? (3)

4) Suggest a synonym for the word 'evade' (line 14). (1)

5) What do you think the word "unambiguously" means? (line 18) (1)

6) Summarise how US textbooks about the Vietnam War have changed since the 1970s. Use information and statistics from the text to support your answer. (4)

7) State whether the following image descriptions would more characteristic of a 1970s textbook or of a 2005 textbook, giving a reason for your answer in each case.

   a) American fighter plane fires at Vietnamese soldiers. (2)
   b) American soldier being treated in a hospital bed for severe injuries. (2)

8) Suggest two possible explanations for the change in the nature of American textbooks on the Vietnam War with time. (2)

9) In focusing on Americans' pain, textbook writers have neglected to address one crucial aspect of the war. What is this aspect and why do you think the authors are reluctant to address it? (2)

Writing Task

You went scuba diving for the very first time at a coral reef. Write a diary entry describing what you experienced. (20)

Marks

Comprehension

Carefully read the passage below and answer ALL of the questions which follow.

A hedgehog explains the body language of trees

Trees are endlessly fascinating organisms with incredible forms, awesome strength and countless uses. I often stand and stare at a particular tree and wonder what it has been through in its life, but to read that tree's biography we need to able to read its body language, visualise its internal structures and assess its weaknesses. When we understand why it has grown in a particular way and why the ripples, bumps and cracks in its bark are where they are, then we can start to unravel its story. There is also another more practical reason for being able to do this however, and that is to avoid the potentially fatal consequences of a tree failing while you are standing underneath it! (lines 1–7)

Several years ago, when I had responsibility for a programme of overnight camps in woodlands, there was a 'near miss' when a branch fell down near a member of staff's tent during the night. Rather than just stop using the site, we paid a consultant to do a detailed survey of all trees in the camp area and submit a detailed report. This was expensive but vitally important to the safety of our staff and groups. It also started a germ of an interest in visually identifying tree hazards myself. The following year, a colleague and I took a one day course in Quantified Tree Risk Assessment, which is a system widely used by local authorities and tree professionals around the world. The methodology seemed sound and especially useful for those concerned with possible litigation however the skill gap to identify potential failures in the first place remained. I was directed to the work of Claus Mattheck, professor of Bio-mechanics at Karlsruhe University who, as well as trees, says he likes hiking, Staffordshire bull terriers and large calibre weapons! Unfortunately the only book I could find at the time was highly technical and cost £70. (lines 8–18)

Then yesterday at the Association of Professional Foresters Exhibition in Warwickshire I found what I really needed in Professor Mattheck's wonderful book 'Stupsi Explains the Tree'. (lines 19–20)

Stupsi is a hedgehog, who, through the author's cartoon drawings explains some quite complex mechanics and tree biology in a very accessible way. There is no index, table of contents or chapter structure to the book but it does move from the simple to more complex ideas in a linear way. (lines 21–23)

The book starts with how wind can affect broadleaved and coniferous trees in different ways and introduces the central idea of tension and compression wood. Stupsi then looks at what patterns in bark and the shape of stems and branches can tell us about the forces at work in the tree and which clues might hint at whether a branch might break or not. The section on hollow trees is especially good and explains well why hollow pollards can live so long. This is followed by lots on the structural role of roots, what may damage them and what the consequences can be for the tree. Urban trees and human impacts on them are covered in the last third of the book and it is only here that we get into the cellular structure of wood and explaining rings and rays in cross sections with the aid of 'lignin chimneys' and 'cellulose hosepipes'. Once this concept is clear we move to understanding how some fungi break down lignin and others attack cellulose which helps explain different types of rot in wood. (lines 24–33)

Each page is laid out with a cartoon of a tree with a particular issue or feature with Stupsi modelling the issue using his body or a prop like a rope or banana. A photograph of an actual tree with this feature helps to illustrate the short cartoony text which avoids most technical language apart from a few terms like 'axiom of uniform stress' and 'tangential compressive stress' that creep in occasionally. Most of us have a rope in our bag and Stupsi's demonstrations could easily be combined with the reader's new knowledge of trees to help explain a particular tree form or hazard to a group in a forest school or other forest education situation. (lines 34–40)

Marks

The ideas are necessarily complex but they are explained to lay people and non-engineers without the use of formulae and with photos and real world analogies. It is a short book that can be read very quickly, but I think it will be necessary to read it again and again and most importantly to take it into the woods when looking at real trees.

In relation to many other environments used for outdoor learning, forests and woodlands rank fairly low in terms of perceived and actual risks. Trees may fall, drop branches or be hit by lightning but these things happen rarely and mostly during particular weather conditions. To assess risks from tree hazards in woodlands we need to account for the time spent under any particular tree as well as correctly identify the hazard. The first part of the equation is straightforward – how big is the group, how often are they there and how much time is spent in particular places. Hazardous trees over our camp present much more of a risk than those which are merely passed by on an occasional walk. 45 50

Identifying which trees and branches should be avoided, pruned or removed however is much more difficult and that is where Stupsi will be an invaluable companion. Having read this slim volume once this morning, I am twitching to head out the back door and look at the trees on the common with different eyes. I don't expect to become an expert overnight but at least now have the basic theory and language to test and explain my hunches. I might not be able to make the most tricky tree hazard judgements myself but will hopefully be better placed to know when I really need to phone an arborist or walk away from a site. 55 57

Written by Richard Irvine / CC 3.0
(http://richardirvine.co.uk/2014/09/the-body-language-of-trees/)

<u>END OF ARTICLE. Please answer the following questions:</u>

1) What happened to spark the author's interest in identifying tree hazards? (2)

2) Suggest a synonym for the word 'unravel' (line 5). (1)

3) Give two reasons why the author purchased 'Stupsi Explains the Tree' and not the first book he saw on the topic. (2)

4) What do you think would be the role of the 'cellulose hosepipe' (line 31) in a tree, and explain your thought process. (2)

5) What two things need to be considered when assessing risks from tree hazards? Which of the two is easier to account for and why? (4)

6) What natural force is described in the text that may cause a tree to fall? Why is this not usually of primary concern? (2)

7) What do you think an 'arborist' (final line) does? When do you think you might need to phone one? (2)

8) Stupsi is aimed not only at beginners to tree hazard perception but also aims to encourage children to gain interest. What does Prof Mattheck do to make his book more appealing to children? (3)

9) What do you think is involved in the study of 'Bio-mechanics' (line 16)? (2)

Writing Task

Should it be compulsory for every student to play a musical instrument? (20)

Marks

Comprehension

Carefully read the passage below and answer ALL of the questions which follow.

<u>The Golden Touch – King Midas</u>

King Midas was a very important person. He owned a huge house with maids and servants in it. King Midas was a friendly man and loved to give and receive love. Bacchus was one of the gods that adored this love and was very generous. 1

"King Midas I will grant you any wish!" Bacchus exclaimed.

"Any wish?" the King replied feeling joyful and happy. 5

"Any wish! You name it and I'll do it!"

"I would like to have the hands of gold. Anything I touch will turn to gold." King Midas said feeling very happy and excited.

"As you wish." Bacchus exclaimed.

The King was now smiling from ear to ear. He went out after the gathering and touched the first thing he saw, a twig on his apple tree. The twig instantly turned to gold. The King started laughing! 10

"It works!" said King Midas.

"Of course!" Bacchus shouted back before leaving.

The day went on and King Midas went around touching items. The stones turned to gold. The sand on the beach changed to grains of gold. Delighted, the King went back to his house. The King called his servants to bring food for him. He picked up a piece of meat with his fork. The fork turned to gold, along with the piece of steak. He laughed. Then he took a piece of bread. He bit into a gold nugget instead of the chewy bread. Now the King was not sure about this wonderful wish. The King started to cry. His tears filled puddles and asked Bacchus to take back the horrible wish. Bacchus looked at the King now on his knees. Bacchus put his hand on the shoulder of the pleading man. 15 20

"How could you ever grant me a horrible wish like that?" the King asked.

"You deserved it! You wanted to be rich but being rich is a big responsibility," Bacchus said.

"Yes, but now all I want is to be normal," said the King

"I will be nice and let you go this time, but you better watch what you wish for," said Bacchus.

"Thank you, my lord." 25

"All you have to do is fully wash yourself in the river and you'll become free from your wish."

"Again, thank you. I will always remember what you said."

And with that the King washed himself head to toe in the river and started touching things. They stayed the same. The King pranced around. He ate a huge dinner and fell asleep. In his dream he was a monkey trapped inside a cage. Then the monkey got freed and he lived happily ever after. The End. 30

<u>END OF ARTICLE. Please answer the following questions:</u>

1) Why did Bacchus grant the king any wish in line 5? (2)

Marks

2) Suggest a synonym for “exclaimed” (line 4). (1)

3) In line 19, the king was “on his knees”. Why? (1)

4) Pick one example of each of the following from the passage: (3)

a) Adjective
b) Personal pronoun
c) Proper noun

5) Why is it that the “The king pranced around” in line 29 and what does “pranced” mean? (2)

6) Who do you think is wiser, King Midas or Bacchus? Why? (3)

7) Using information from the text, determine whether the following statements are true, false or more information is needed to be sure.

a) King Midas turned bread into steak. (1)
b) Bacchus is the Roman God of gold. (1)
c) The King needed only wash his hands in the river to become free of his wish. (1)
d) The king was desperate to reverse the effect of his wish. (1)
e) The king could not turn food to gold. (1)

8) In lines 29-30 the king had a dream. Draw comparisons between this dream and the rest of the story. (3)

Writing Task

Use the picture shown as inspiration for a piece of creative writing. Marks will be given for imaginative descriptions and correct use of vocabulary, punctuation and grammar. (20)

Photo credits to **Ministry of Information Photo Division Photographer / Public Domain** (https://commons.wikimedia.org/wiki/File:A_Picture_of_a_Southern_Town-_Life_in_Wartime_Reading,_Berkshire,_England,_UK,_1945_D25417.jpg)

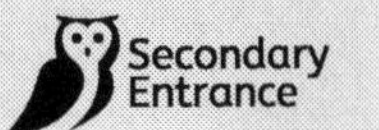

Marks

Comprehension

Carefully read the passage below and answer ALL of the questions which follow.

Ours to Hack and to Own

It seems like the age of ownership is over, and I'm not just talking about the devices and software that many of us bring into our homes and our lives. I'm also talking about the platforms and services on which those devices and apps rely. 1

While many of the services that we use are free, we don't have any control over them. The firms that do, in essence, control what we see, what we hear, and what we read. Not only that, but many of them are also changing the nature of work. They're using closed platforms to power a shift away from full-time work to the gig economy, one that offers little in the way of security or certainty. 5

This move has wide-ranging implications for the Internet and for everyone who uses and relies on it. The vision of the open Internet from just 20-odd-years ago is fading and is rapidly being replaced by an impenetrable curtain. 10

One remedy that's becoming popular is building platform cooperatives, which are digital platforms that their users own. The idea behind platform cooperatives has many of the same roots as open source, as the book "Ours to Hack and to Own" explains.

Scholar Trebor Scholz and writer Nathan Schneider have collected 40 essays discussing the rise of, and the need for, platform cooperatives as tools ordinary people can use to promote openness, and to counter the opaqueness and the restrictions of closed systems. 15

Where open source fits in

At or near the core of any platform cooperative lies open source; not necessarily open source technologies, but the principles and the ethos that underlie open source—openness, transparency, cooperation, collaboration, and sharing. 20

In his introduction to the book, Trebor Scholz points out that:

In opposition to the black-box systems of the Snowden-era Internet, these platforms need to distinguish themselves by making their data flows transparent. They need to show where the data about customers and workers are stored, to whom they are sold, and for what purpose.

It's that transparency, so essential to open source, which helps make platform cooperatives so appealing and a refreshing change from much of what exists now. 25

Open source software can definitely play a part in the vision of platform cooperatives that "Ours to Hack and to Own" shares. Open source software can provide a fast, inexpensive way for groups to build the technical infrastructure that can power their cooperatives.

Mickey Metts illustrates this in the essay, "Meet Your Friendly Neighbourhood Tech Co-Op." Metts works for a firm called Agaric, which uses Drupal to build for groups and small business what they otherwise couldn't do for themselves. On top of that, Metts encourages anyone wanting to build and run their own business or co-op to embrace free and open source software. Why? It's high quality, it's inexpensive, you can customize it, and you can connect with large communities of helpful, passionate people. 30

Not always about open source, but open source is always there 35

Marks

Not all of the essays in this book focus or touch on open source; however, the key elements of the open source way—cooperation, community, open governance, and digital freedom—are always on or just below the surface.

In fact, as many of the essays in "Ours to Hack and to Own" argue, platform cooperatives can be important building blocks of a more open, commons-based economy and society. That can be, in Douglas Rushkoff's words, organisations like Creative Commons compensating "for the privatization of shared intellectual resources." It can also be what Francesca Bria, Barcelona's CTO, describes as cities running their own "distributed common data infrastructures with systems that ensure the security and privacy and sovereignty of citizens' data." 40

Final thought 45

If you're looking for a blueprint for changing the Internet and the way we work, "Ours to Hack and to Own" isn't it. The book is more a manifesto than user guide. Having said that, "Ours to Hack and to Own" offers a glimpse at what we can do if we apply the principles of the open source way to society and to the wider world. 49

Written by **Scott Nesbitt** for **Open Source / CC 4.0**
(https://opensource.com/article/17/1/review-book-ours-to-hack-and-own)

END OF ARTICLE. Please answer the following questions:

1) Give three benefits of open source according to Mickey Metts. (2)

2) Using information from the text, determine whether the following statements are true, false or more information is needed to be sure.

   a) Nathan Schneider was the author of the book's introduction. (1)
   b) All of the essays in the book at least touch on –or focus on– open source. (1)
   c) Platform cooperatives are owned by the company from which users purchase them. (1)
   d) Full time work provides more security and is more profitable than gig work. (1)
   e) "Ours to Hack and to Own" is essentially just a user guide for changing the way we work. (1)

3) Regarding platform cooperatives, what aspects of their data storage must they show to distinguish themselves from older systems? (2)

4) Select one example of each of the following from the text;

   a) Preposition (1)
   b) Personal Pronoun (1)
   c) Conjunction (1)

5) Quoting from the text, explain what you think is meant by the term "open Internet" (line 9)? (2)

6) Select one metaphor from the text and explain why you think the author included it. (2)

7) "the privatization of shared intellectual resources" (lines 41-42). Simplify in your own words the meaning of this phrase as best you can. (2)

8) "promote openness, and to counter the opaqueness" (line 15-16). Comment on the author's use of language here, and how this helps him communicate his point. (2)

Writing Task

Write a diary entry from the perspective of a time traveller from the year 2017 who has travelled to the year 3000. (20)

Marks

Comprehension

Carefully read the passage below and answer ALL of the questions which follow.

Diwali

SUNDAY, OCTOBER 30: The worldwide festival of lights launches from India today, in the ancient Hindu celebration of Diwali. In recognition of the triumph of light over darkness, Diwali bears great significance for Hindus, Jains and Sikhs alike. As awareness of Indian culture spreads, major celebrations now are hosted around the world. And, please note: *Dates and spellings of Diwali vary by country and region.* 1

Preparations for Diwali begin weeks in advance, so a flurry of pre-Diwali activity can be seen in most cities of India. In a shopping extravaganza comparable to the Western Christmas season, gold jewellery, fine clothing, sweet treats and household goods fly off racks in marketplaces across India. At home, surfaces are scrubbed clean, women and children decorate entrances with Rangoli and men string strands of lights. Official celebrations begin two days before Diwali, and end two days after Diwali—spanning a total of five days. During this five-day period, the old year closes and a new year is rung in. 5 10

Did you know? Diwali is derived from the Sanskrit fusion of diya *("light," or "lamp") and* avali *("series," "line," or "row"). For Diwali, rows of lamps are lit in homes and temples.*

On Diwali, excitement builds as evening approaches. While donning new clothing, *diyas* (earthen lamps, filled with oil) are lit, prayers are offered to deities and many households welcome Lakshmi, the goddess of wealth and prosperity who is believed to roam the earth on Diwali night. The night's extravaganza is a sky ablaze with fireworks. Families gather for a feast of sweets and desserts as the *diyas* remain lit through the dark hours. 15

The day following Diwali is *Padwa*, honouring the mutual love between husbands and wives. The next day, *Bhai Duj*, celebrates the sister-brother bond. On *Bhai Duj*, women and girls gather to perform puja and prayers for the well-being of their brothers, and siblings engage in gift-giving and the sharing of a meal. 20

ATMAN, HIGHER KNOWLEDGE

Several Hindu schools of philosophy teach the existence of something beyond the physical body and mind: something pure and infinite, known as *atman*. Diwali celebrates the victory of good over evil, in the deeper meaning of higher knowledge dissipating ignorance and hope prevailing over despair. When truth is realised, Hindus believe that one can see past ignorance and into the oneness of all things. 25

Marks

DIWALI AMONG JAINS AND SIKHS

On the night of Diwali, Jains celebrate light for yet another reason: to mark the attainment of *moksha*, or nirvana, by Mahavira. As the final Jain Tirthankar of this era, Mahavira's attainment is celebrated with much fervour. It's believed that many gods were present on the night when Mahavira reached moksha, and that their presence illuminated the darkness. 30

Sikhs mark the Bandi Chhor Divas on Diwali, when Guru Har Gobind Ji freed himself and the Hindu kings from Fort Gwalior and arrived at the Golden Temple in Amritsar. Today, Bandi Chhor Divas is commemorated with the lighting of the Golden Temple, fireworks and more. 33

Written by Anonymous for Read The Spirit / CC 3.0
(https://www.readthespirit.com/religious-holidays-festivals/tag/festival-of-lights/)

END OF ARTICLE. Please answer the following questions:

1) On what exact date did official Diwali celebrations commence in the year that this article was written? (1)

2) What is the English translation of the word 'diwali'? (1)

3) What is the meaning of the word 'donning' (line 13)? (1)

4) From the text, give one example of each of the following:

   a) Something bought in preparation for Diwali. (1)
   b) The name of one of the days immediately following Diwali. (1)
   c) Something used to decorate people's homes. (1)

5) Describe briefly the slight differences in the significance of Diwali to Hindus, Jains and Sikhs. Include quotations from the text to support your answer. (6)

6) Imagine you are a small child at home on the evening of Diwali. Write a short piece detailing your excitement at your environment, mentioning the sights, sounds and other senses you experience. Marks will be awarded for creative language and the overall quality of your language. (8)

Writing Task

Should students be allowed to leave school during their lunchtime break? (20)

Marks

Comprehension

Carefully read the passage below and answer ALL of the questions which follow.

Face to face with the Gorilla King

The day started out okay. Well it was a bit boring if I am honest. We got up, got dressed and had breakfast. I wore my "Nature is wild" t-shirt. It's really cool with a picture of a small deer in the mouth of a large lion. Mum doesn't like it but I insisted that this was the perfect day to wear it. We had breakfast and set out to catch the train to the zoo. Dad had taken the day off so the whole family could go, it being half term and all. Mum fussed over whether I was warm enough and Dad strode off at a heck of a pace towards the station. All pretty much normal. The train journey was fairly uneventful as well. After a quick change onto another line we arrived at the zoo in good time. The penguins were nearer to the entrance so we went there first. They were pretty cute I have to say and the way they walked was quite funny. They're swimming was amazing, particularly when you looked through the glass walls into the tank. I guess I should have realised something was up though as at one point I crawled into a bubble window to see the inside of tank and suddenly all the penguins swam over towards me. For a second I thought they were pointing at me but as I turned to tell my Dad the keeper arrived with a bucket of fish and they all swam off towards her.

Something similar happened at the reptile house. When I looked into the Komodo dragon enclosure one of them spotted me and, quick as a flash, ran over towards me. Others spotted it and ran over as well. By the time we had covered half the zoo I was getting very worried. Not only were the zoo animals apparently attracted to me but also there was a growing collection of seagulls, pigeons and insects all seemingly following me. We asked a zookeeper what might be the problem but he just said the animals probably mixed me up with a keeper and came over for food. When I asked why the birds and insects were following me, he said I was probably imagining it and they often hang around the zoo.

If he had been with us at the ape house he would have changed his mind. The pride of the zoo is a large silverback called Titan. You'd recognise him from all the posters, bags, t-shirts, caps, badges, stickers, mugs and stationery with his picture on. When we arrived he was sitting in a hammock strung between two trees. As soon as we turned the corner and could see him, he started staring at me. Then, slowly he got up and walked over to our side of the enclosure. Normally being approached by a gorilla of that size would be quite frightening, but we had a wall and a deep, wide pit between us so I wasn't that worried. I was surprised though because he wouldn't take his eyes off me. Actually as he got close I realised he couldn't take his eyes off my t-shirt.

"Do you like this shirt?" I asked in a patronising voice. The gorilla just stared at me then turned and walked away again. He disappeared into the buildings at the back of the enclosure and after a while reappeared with something in his hand. It looked like a brick but as he got closer I saw that it was a piece of carved, dark wood. I have to say I was transfixed. I stood there watching the huge, magnificent animal as it strode around the enclosure. He climbed up onto a platform and sat down. The wood was still in his hand and he held it up to his mouth as if to chew it. Suddenly he launched it high into the air and we all looked to see it flying towards us. It landed with a clatter behind me. Nobody spoke but some let out a gasp. The gorilla looked me in the eye and gestured towards the piece of wood behind me. Did he want me to throw it back? If so I doubt I could get it across the trench, let alone as far as the platform. I turned and went over to it.

"Don't touch it!" Dad said, "You might catch germs from the gorilla."

"Or pass some onto him," Mum added.

"He wants me to throw it back." I said, bending down to it. The carving was very intricate and detailed. I could see what looked like writing on the underside and, without thinking, I turned it over. As soon as I touched it there was a bright flash of white light and all of the noises of the zoo stopped. I must have passed out because for a second I couldn't see. Then gradually my sight returned and I realised I was lying on the floor. I stood up and brushed myself down. That was when I realised the floor had changed. Where there had been concrete, now there was polished marble. Also, where I had been out in the open before, now I was in a large room. Around the edges of the room were ornate chairs and the walls were decorated with silk fabric of the richest blues, purples and reds. The chairs were carved and covered in gold. In each chair sat an occupant who held a white tube about a quarter of a metre long with gold caps on the ends.

Each occupant was an ape of some kind. There were orangutans with large heads, chimpanzees sitting crossed-legs and gorillas with stern looks on their faces. I saw a wide strip of purple carpet stretch from some huge doors to a set of steps at one end of the room. At the top of the steps was a large, golden throne with long waves of white silk draped over it. On the throne sat a large silverback gorilla who leaned towards

Marks

me and beckoned me with a finger. I stood rooted to the spot. I had no idea whether this was a dream or not but even if it was, it was one of the weirdest I'd ever had. The silverback again beckoned me closer with its finger. I started to walk towards the throne when a cough to one side made me turn and look. One of the chimps was bowing its head and indicated I should do the same. I did, and continued walking until I reached the edge of the carpet. Not knowing what to do next I stood there, with my head bowed. 55

The silverback stood and walked down the steps to me. It took my chin gently in its hand and turned my head to each side as if inspecting it. I have to say I was petrified. I knew enough about gorillas to know that with one arm this creature could deliver a blow which would kill me. After a few moments of this inspection the silverback let go of my chin and stepped back a bit. Then something really weird happened and, considering what kind of day it had been, that's saying something. The silverback spoke. It looked around the room and spoke with a loud, deep voice. 60

"So this is the one. This is the human child the prophecy speaks of?"

An orangutan stood and spoke "Lord Titan seems quite certain of it my king. He says he was told the boy had arrived at the zoo but refused to believe it. When the child arrived at the enclosure Lord Titan saw for himself and was immediately convinced." 65

"This cloth the child wears," the silverback replied, stroking my shirt, "how close to the description in the prophecy is it?"

"It is a perfect match my king," the orangutan responded.

"Then he must be the one," the gorilla said. Then it turned to me and said "And you child, what do you have to say for yourself, can you do it?" 70

I suppose saying something, anything would have helped but all I could do was stand there with my mouth open. 73

Written by Ryan Cartwright for Crimper Books / CC 3.0
(https://crimperbooks.co.uk/short-stories/gorilla-king-short-story-for-kids-part-1/)

END OF ARTICLE. Please answer the following questions:

1) Give two instances where the author aims to highlight that this was initially an ordinary day. (2)

2) What two reasons did the boy's parents give to persuade him not to touch the wood that the gorilla had thrown to him? (2)

3) Using information from the text, determine whether the following statements are true, false or more information is needed to be sure.

   a) Lord Titan is a gorilla. (1)
   b) The boy's T-shirt showed a picture of a large gorilla. (1)
   c) Titan was sitting in a tyre swing when the boy arrived. (1)
   d) Titan was wearing a white cape. (1)
   e) A wide red carpet ran from the steps to the doors of the room. (1)

4) Define the word "transfixed" (line 30) and suggest a synonym for this word. (2)

5) Re-read lines 43-47. What kind of place does it sound like the boy has been transported to? Give two items/descriptions mentioned in the text to support your answer. (3)

6) Write a short continuation of the story. Marks will be awarded for exciting narrative, descriptive language as well as spelling, punctuation and grammar. (6)

Writing Task

Continue the following piece of creative writing:

"Wake up, wake up! Come and see!" Lucy's dad cried.
Lucy sleepily opened her eyes to see him excitedly gesturing at the window. Groaning and yawning, she stumbled out of bed, dragging her blanket behind her to go and take a look... (20)

Marks

Comprehension

Carefully read the passage below and answer ALL of the questions which follow.

The game worlds we make

I passed an embarrassing number of hours in my fifth and sixth-grade years alone in my room, wrestling with the mathematics of probability. I would lie on my rug, hand-writing tables on legal pads and cardboard, rows and rows of numbers delineating the likelihood of one outcome over another. I built elaborate statistical models to account for how changing one variable might affect the overall system. I tinkered with different methods for generating random numbers so that the system could more accurately represent the impact of chance. (1, 5)

If this sounds like I am showing off, I should add one crucial detail to the account: I was expending all this mental energy designing dice baseball games. Those of you who grew up before *Madden* and the PS4 might remember this genre: sports simulations like APBA and Strat-o-Matic where you could manage or coach virtual teams—represented by paper cards, not pixels on a screen—or create fantasy matchups. Ty Cobb going to bat against Sandy Koufax; the giants of the dead-ball era playing against Bronx Bombers. I had spent my third and fourth-grade years exploring the existing offerings in this genre, but by the time I turned 11, I found myself seeking out even more accuracy in the simulations. Could you build a game that might allow you to choose between throwing a slider and a fastball? Could the model account for the varying shapes of different ballparks: Fenway's Green Monster, the vast centre field of the original Polo Grounds? (10, 15)

All of us walk around with a set of expectations about what proper learning experiences are supposed to look like: reading a book, preparing for an exam, listening to a lecture, watching an educational video. I couldn't see it at the time, of course, but that experience of designing my own baseball simulations turned out to be one of the great educational experiences of my childhood—for reasons I am only now beginning to understand, watching my own kids explore their game worlds, onscreen and off. The irony is that I spent almost no time enjoying the games I created. I couldn't persuade any friends to come over and learn the arcane rules that I had scribbled out on a legal pad, and it wasn't all that much fun to play on my own. It was always more captivating to tinker with the structure of the latest game, or start dreaming up a new one, with added levels of accuracy or strategic depth. I spent all my time designing the rules for play, but almost never managed to make it to the part where you *actually play*. Designing the rules turned out to be too much fun. (20, 25)

A few years ago, I decided to revisit the game design obsessions of my childhood. This time with a collaborator: my youngest son, Dean, who was nine years old at the time. None of my kids picked up on my youthful obsession with sabermetrics (or with any professional sports for that matter, other than a passing interest in European football) and so a sports simulation was out of the question. We were living in Northern California at the time and, at the risk of self-parody, my son was going to an organic farming camp in Petaluma that summer. So after some discussion, we decided that the game should have a farming theme. We started calling it *Blossom*—which we both agreed was a terrible name for a board game, but we ended up getting so distracted by the game design that we never bothered to go back and come up with a more compelling alternative. (30, 35)

I've never been one for parenting advice columns or books, but if you haven't designed a board game with your child, you should really grab some cardboard, scissors, and magic markers; steal some dice from that *Monopoly* set you have lying around; and get to work. It's one of those magical parent-child activities where the two of you occupy shared ground in terms of both comprehension and engagement. Even simple games present intellectually interesting puzzles for an adult brain in their design phase, and children are incredibly adept at picking up on the nuances of gameplay. (40)

So much of parenting is forcing yourself to be interested in stories or explanations that you grew acclimated to decades before, drawing on your child's infectious curiosity to get you excited about experiences that had long ago lost their interest. But a new game—a game where everything about it is up for grabs—is a blank slate. And your expertise as a game designer is really not all that more advanced than your nine-year-old's. Game design is one of those rare experiences that brings out the child in you, and the adult in your child. (45)

I had suspected from the outset that designing the game with Dean would be rewarding purely as a parent-child bonding exercise. But I hadn't fully realised—until we actually sat down and started plotting out the game—how powerful the experience would be as a kind of mental exercise. Even the simplest game involves layers of creativity and analysis that rival anything your average nine-year-old is doing in school. You can separate out those layers in retrospect, but in practice they are all happening simultaneously as you work on the project. (50, 53)

Written by Stephen Johnson for How to Get on Next / CC 4.0
(https://howwegettonext.com/the-game-worlds-we-make-3662708f92f6)

END OF ARTICLE. Please answer the following questions:

Marks

1) Comment on the author's use of the word 'wrestling' (line 2). (1)

2) Why was it decided that the game that the author and his son made should be based around farming? And why was the game's initial name never changed? (2)

3) "Those of you who grew up before *Madden* and the PS4 might remember this genre" (lines 8-9). What is the effect of the use of the word 'you' here? (1)

4) What is Fenway's Green Monster? (1)

5) From the text, select one example of each of the following:

   a) A baseball player. (1)
   b) An ordinal number (1)
   c) An adjective (1)

6) Name two things the author suggests you might need to design a board game. (2)

7) Give four quotations from the text which demonstrate that the author feels that building a board game with one's child is a great idea. (4)

8) Using information from the text, determine whether the following statements are true, false or more information is needed to be sure.

   a) Dean is the author's only child. (1)
   b) Petaluma is in Western California. (1)
   c) The author often gives parenting advice to other people. (1)
   d) As a child, the author spent hours each day playing the games he had designed. (1)
   e) The authors cannot afford to buy his son a PS4. (1)

9) What does 'in retrospect' (line 52) mean? (1)

Writing Task

Use the picture shown as inspiration for a piece of creative writing. Marks will be given for imaginative descriptions and correct use of vocabulary, punctuation and grammar. (20)

Photo credits to **Pexels / CC0**
https://pixabay.com/p-1842308/?no_redirect

Marks

Comprehension

Carefully read the passage below and answer ALL of the questions which follow.

A day at the beach

The vibrant, summer sun kissed my cheek and a subtle breeze swept across my face as I looked onward across the horizon. A lone seagull swooped down towards the sea front before climbing back up into the brilliant sky, its eyes fixed on an oblivious fish, gently fighting the tide. 1

Time seemed to move slowly, even more so as an onlooker. The sea shimmered like a diamond. A toddler eagerly tiptoed his way towards the edge of the water, and as the tide came in, he shrieked with joy as the cooling water tickled his feet, and as he turned around, he smiled once again at the sight of his mother, beckoning him back with open arms; his blue eyes and smooth skin speckled with grains of sand. He waddled as fast as his little feet could carry him, his mouth open as his giggled through the deep and seemingly unfamiliar terrain of sand, before his mother wrapped him up tightly into a towel, her nose rubbing against his cheek as she kissed him. 5 10

I was lying near the road. Next to the road a pavement was the only barrier before the path which led down to the beach, the tips of umbrellas peaking up above it, making it even more inviting. A kite soared up into the sky, swooping like the seagull up and down, and a proud grandfather stood with his arms crossed, chuckling at his grandson, who, biting his lip in concentration, tugged at the kite as he tried to keep it airborne. The child turned his head in my direction, and for a second we shared eye contact, before he turned to his grandfather, handed him the kite, and ran towards me. The grandfather, surprised at the child's sudden change in interest looked in my direction, and also seemed to run. 15

There was a larger crowd of people gathering around where I was lying yet I was oblivious to this, for my interest was in the child running up towards me. The sound of the ambulance had been gradually getting louder, yet it was only now that I realised it was only a few feet away. Dozens of eyes seems to be looking at me, and a constant muffled murmuring could be heard. My wife, she was crying, her arm stretched out towards me, yet she was held back by those neighbouring her. She fell to her knees, exhausted, before pounding the ground as she looked up to the heavens, asking them for a reason why her husband had been chosen, and at a time she needed him most. 20

The man of the car that hit me was also there, but he continued to stare at me, emotionless, his eyes glazed with shock. A man in a yellow and green jacket approached me feverishly, cautiously dodging the stray pieces of glass from the windscreen, which were scattered like mines around my body. A cold stream 25

Marks

of blood slipped down the side of my cheek and spilt out onto the ground in front of me. I turned my gaze, and as the man in the jacket anxiously tried along with others to unravel a stretcher from the back of the ambulance, I remembered that peace I had felt. I looked into the eyes of my trembling son, and as much as I tried to stay awake, I could do nothing but succumb to the enchanting power which had captured me, just one minute ago. 30 32

Written by Suraj Joshi

END OF ARTICLE. Please answer the following questions:

1) From the passage above, select one example of each of the following:

   a) Simile (1)
   b) Imagery (1)
   c) Emotive language (1)

2) Line 3 reads: “its eyes fixed on an oblivious fish”. Suggest another word that could replace ‘oblivious’ in this case, without changing the meaning of the sentence. (1)

3) In line 14, the child is “biting his lip in concentration”. What is he concentrating on? (1)

4) Give three examples of adjectives used to describe the writer’s surroundings. (3)

5) “A man in a yellow and green jacket approached me” (lines 26). Who is this man? (1)

6) “I was lying near the road.” Comment on this sentence. How does it contribute to the change in tone of the story? (3)

7) Re-read lines 18-32. Give two ways the writer creates a sense of drama here, providing quotations to support your points. (4)

8) Re-read the final paragraph (lines 25-32). Give two ways the writer portrays a sense of danger, using quotations to support your argument. (4)

Writing Task

Write a story with the title ‘Waves’. Marks will be given for imaginative descriptions and correct use of vocabulary, punctuation and grammar. (20)

Marks

Comprehension

Carefully read the passage below and answer ALL of the questions which follow.

How conifers overcome their seasonal affective disorder

Evergreen conifers face a unique challenge during winter: it is too cold for photosynthesis, but their leaves still absorb light energy. This can be dangerous to leaf tissues if the absorbed light energy is not dissipated. Plants can get rid of excess light energy absorbed by light harvesting complexes through the xanthophyll cycle, whereby a pigment called violaxanthin (which absorbs light energy for use in photosynthesis) is converted to zeaxanthin (which converts light energy to heat) under stressful light conditions. Conifers have both a rapidly and slowly reversible form of energy dissipation (via the xanthophyll cycle) for winter stress, and the rapid form disengages above 0°C, while the slow form is maintained throughout winter. (lines 1–8)

In a recent article in *Tree Physiology*, Ryan Merry and colleagues (2017) sought to determine how two evergreen conifers, Eastern white pine (*Pinus strobus*) and white spruce (*Picea glauca*), recover from winter stress. To look at recovery, they cut branches from trees throughout the winter, took them indoors, and looked at how the leaf biochemistry changed under warmer temperatures. They found that pine took up to three times longer than spruce to recover photosynthetic function. The rapid form of energy dissipation was only obvious in one case for pine, but in all cases for spruce demonstrating that pine may be more dependent on the slow mechanism of photosynthetic recovery than spruce. These differences between pine and spruce were also associated with changes in the phosphorylation status of key photosynthetic proteins. Dephosphorylation, the removal of a phosphate group from a protein, is a process used to regulate protein function over short to long time scales. Since the dephosphorylation of light harvesting complexes was faster in spruce than pine, the authors hypothesize that this process may regulate the rapidly reversible component of energy dissipation in evergreen conifers. (lines 9–20)

Since white spruce can respond more rapidly during recovery from winter stress than Eastern white pine, this could allow white spruce to outcompete Eastern white pine, by allowing greater and earlier growth during spring. These differences between pine and spruce are important to consider at the ecosystem level. If winter recovery is treated the same way for pine and spruce in ecosystem models and climate projections, model predictions could be very wrong. This could be particularly important when there are frequent freeze-thaw cycles, which would cause changes in the rapid component of energy dissipation and divergent (lines 21–26)

Marks

environmental responses in pine and spruce. Thus, it appears that white spruce is faster than Eastern white pine at overcoming the winter blues. 28

Written by Joseph Stinziano for AOB Blog / CC 4.0
(https://aobblog.com/2017/06/recovering-winter-conifers-overcome-seasonal-affective-disorder/)

END OF ARTICLE. Please answer the following questions:

1) Why do you think these trees are referred to as 'evergreen' (line 1)? (2)

2) What unique danger do conifers face in the winter? Name and describe the mechanism they use to solve this problem. (4)

3) What biochemical process can organisms use to regulate protein function over time? Describe what occurs in this process. (2)

4) Do you think this article is aimed at people with no knowledge of plant science, good knowledge, or leading experts in the field? Justify your answer using reference to the text. (3)

5) What do you think is meant by the term "freeze-thaw cycles" (line 26)? (2)

6) State whether the Eastern white pine or white spruce outcompeted the other, and explain why it was able to do so. (3)

7) Using information from the text, determine whether the following statements are true, false or more information is needed to be sure.

   a) Merry and his colleagues solely looked at sections of tree bark under the microscope to determine biochemical changes at warmer temperatures. (1)
   b) It was concluded that the white spruce is able to rebound from winter more quickly as it has larger leaves so starts photosynthesizing more quickly. (1)
   c) Both the trees mentioned are commonly found in the Far East in countries such as China. (1)
   d) Dephosphorylation regulates protein function in the short term, but not the long term. (1)

Writing Task

Write a speech in which you discuss the negative effects that man has on the environment. (20)

Marks

Comprehension

Carefully read the passage below and answer ALL of the questions which follow.

Waiting at the bus stop

It was raining. It always rained after craft club. Alice hated that because it meant her artwork either got wet or crumpled as she tried to stuff it in her bag for protection. She looked at Jack who was inspecting his creation intently. 1

"What was it again?" she asked.
"You know very well it's a door hanger," said Jack. 5
"You should keep it out of the rain," Simon said, "it'll get ruined."
Jack shrugged, "I can't put it in my bag because the glitter isn't dry."
"Glitter!" the others laughed.
"Yep!" Jack said, "best way to do the stars." He gingerly held up his door hanger so as not to let the glue run. 10
"Well, mine's dry," Simon declared, "so now it's safely in my bag."
"Not that bit," Alice commented, pointing at a corner of green paper poking through the zip.
"Rats!" said Simon. "It must have got caught. It'll rip when I try to undo the zip now."

Alice looked at her poster again. She was quite pleased with it really. It was a picture of Wendy sewing Peter Pan's shadow back onto his feet. She wasn't too happy with the way Wendy had turned out but using black net curtains as the shadow was a great idea. Jack's door hanger was a picture of Superman flying through space. He'd run a bit short of time and so had cut out Superman's face from a magazine. Only after he stuck it down, did he notice that the man he'd cut out had a beard. Jack snorted as he saw it. 15

"Looks pretty good," Simon said.
"He has a beard," Jack said, "a beard!" 20
"Well he still looks like Superman to me," Alice said.
"Yeah, I s'pose," Jack sighed, "I just wanted it to be better than this."
"What is this obsession with Superman?" Simon asked. He had joined the school at the beginning of term so he didn't really know about Jack and Superman.
"I just love everything about him: the costume, the stories, his powers," Jack said. 25
"Do you ever wish you could fly?" Simon asked.
Jack nodded, "Yeah but if I had a superpower it wouldn't be flying. It would be invisibility. That would be way cooler."
"Why would you want to be invisible?" Simon snorted, "I think flying is better."
"Well if you're invisible, you could walk right out of school and nobody would know," Jack said. 30
"Yes they would," Alice said, "they'd know because they couldn't see you and then you'd get an absence mark."
"So?" Jack said. "You could play football in the park instead. Imagine being able to go past defenders without them seeing you!"
"They'd see the ball though," Simon said, "and they'd just take it off you." 35
"Ah but they couldn't see my feet could they?" Jack smirked. "So why do you want to fly?"
"Well I wouldn't have to wait for this bus then would I?" Simon laughed. "And it would save me walking upstairs ever again."
Jack looked up at the dark clouds above the bus shelter, "Bet you wouldn't like flying in this weather though?" 40
"Easy! I'd fly above the clouds," Simon proclaimed, indicating with his hand how he would do that.
"That's pretty high you know?" Jack said. "You might not be able to breathe up there."
"I'd have the power to hold my breath for hours then," said Simon.
"You can't have two!" Jack said, "one power only."
"But Superman has loads!" Simon said. 45
"Yes but we're talking about what power you would like to have – not *powers*," Jack retorted. Then he turned to Alice, "What about you Alice?"
"Hmm?" Alice said, not really listening. She had been caught daydreaming again, staring at her feet, dangling from the bench.
"What superpower would you most like to have?" Jack asked with a sigh. 50
"Oh I don't know. I hadn't really thought about it."
"You must have!" Simon said. "Everyone knows their favourite superpower!"

Jack thought this was probably not true, but it did seem odd that Alice hadn't thought about it.

"So go on then, think about it now, what power would you like to have?"

Alice pondered and looked at her poster again. 55

Marks

Then she smiled and said, "I suppose having a detachable shadow would be fun."

There was a stunned silence from the others. Whatever they were expecting her to say, it wasn't that.

"What?" Jack said.
Alice nodded at her poster, "Like Peter Pan. Having a shadow which you could detach would be fun."
"Err, no, it wouldn't," scoffed Simon, "I mean what good is that? You're hardly going to save the world or catch a crime lord with a detachable shadow are you?" 60
Alice smiled, "Well maybe I don't want the power for that. Maybe I want it for other reasons."
Jack was still stunned by her choice. "Such as?" he said.
"Such as always having someone to talk to or play with," Alice replied.
"What?!" Simon blurted, "you can't very well play football with your shadow! The ball would go through it!" 65
"And..." Jack added, "how could you talk to a shadow, it hasn't got ears – just shadows of your ears."
"I didn't say it had to hear me," said Alice, "just that it would be nice to have someone to talk to. To tell about how your day has been. That kind of thing."
"Surely you can talk to your shadow now though," Jack said, "it doesn't have to be detached, does it?" 70
"No," Alice smiled, shaking her head, "but it would be nice if it was. It could help you carry large things or fetch your homework if you forgot it."
"That's what brothers are for!" Simon smirked.
"I don't have one of those," Alice said, "or a sister. It's just me and my shadow."
"I still think flying is a cooler power to have," Simon said. 75
"That's because you have so little imagination, Simon," Alice smiled.

The bus pulled up as she said this and the boys got on first. Just before Alice climbed on, Jack saw that she stopped and turned to the bench. She smiled and gestured with her head as if someone was supposed to follow her. 79

Written by Ryan Cartwright for Crimper Books / CC 3.0
(https://crimperbooks.co.uk/short-stories/short-story-waiting-at-the-bus-stop/)

<u>END OF ARTICLE. Please answer the following questions:</u>

1) Answer the following short questions about the passage.

   a) Why did Alice not like it when it rained after craft club? (1)
   b) Why did Jack not put his artwork in his bag like the others? (1)
   c) Why was Jack not happy with how his artwork turned out in the end? (1)
   d) Which of the three children do we know for certain is an only child? Provide evidence from the text to support your answer. (2)

2) How did Alice and Simon try to convince Jack that invisibility was not a good superpower to pick? (2)

3) Regarding Alice's superpower:

   a) What was Alice's chosen superpower? (1)
   b) Where do you think she get the idea from? (1)
   c) How did she justify her choice? (2)

4) Give two synonyms for the word 'pondered' (line 55) (2)

5) Find the following in the text:

   a) Adverb (1)
   b) Personal pronoun (1)
   c) Conjunction (1)

6) Give three reasons why we know that Superman is Jack's favourite superhero. (3)

7) Re-read the final three lines of the passage. Who do you think Alice is gesturing to? (1)

Writing Task

Write an essay about the place that you feel safest. (20)

Marks

Comprehension

Carefully read the passage below and answer ALL of the questions which follow.

Cracker Barrel Style French Toast

At the end of October we went on vacation to Florida (there will be a post, because my four year old went on Tower of Terror and loved it...that needs to be shared with the world). On the drive home we stopped at Cracker Barrel for dinner, as we do every year, except everyone felt like breakfast, so that's what we ordered. 1

In an instant, everything that I knew about French toast changed. If you've had it there, you know. If you haven't, well, you're in for a treat. 5

It's so simple too. The ---1--- to perfect French toast is this: sourdough bread.

I saw that in the menu, and for a second I doubted. Really, sourdough bread. It's not that I don't like it, it's just that I use it for croutons, or for a bit of tang when we're having a steak. I thought *how could that slightly tangy bread work as a sweet-ish breakfast?* The answer – perfectly. 10

That slight tang helps to ---2--- the ---3--- of the maple syrup. The hearty crumb of the bread itself means that it's not soggy, at all, anywhere. It's like sourdough bread was MADE to become French toast, just nobody knows yet. Well, except for Cracker Barrel and anyone else out there that was smarter than me.

As soon as we got home I started working on it. Sophie and I were having it for lunch, and I was calling Bo to rub it in that he was missing it. I will never again make French toast on regular white bread, and you shouldn't either! 15

The ingredients are super simple too; it doesn't need a lot of extra fluff. I don't even add cinnamon to it; I found the flavour to be better without. Just eggs, milk, vanilla, and sugar. Four ingredients, whisked together by ---4--- for thirty ---5---, to give you the ultimate French toast. Your weekend just got a whole lot better! 20

Instructions:

Weigh out and whisk together the eggs, milk, vanilla, and sugar in a medium bowl until well combined.

Heat your pan or griddle to medium-high and grease lightly with butter.

Dip your slices of sourdough in the egg mixture, making sure to coat both sides. Place into your pan, and cook until lightly browned, about 2-3 minutes, then flip and cook the second side. 25

Serve warm with your favourite toppings (butter, warm maple syrup, whipped cream, fresh berries, etc). 26

Marks

Written by Katrina for Kitchen Trials / CC 3.0
(https://www.kitchentrials.com/2015/11/24/cracker-barrel-style-french-toast/)

END OF ARTICLE. Please answer the following questions:

1) Five words from the above passage have been removed, and each word assigned a number. Here is a list of words; select the word in each case which you think BEST fits the meaning of the passage in each case. (5)

hours heart balance stickiness hand
answer recipe seconds help sweetness

1.	
2.	
3.	
4.	
5.	

2) Was this the family's first visit to Cracker Barrel? What time of day did they arrive at? (2)

3) How long do you think this recipe would take to make in total? Justify your answer. (2)

a) 30 seconds
b) 2-3 minutes
c) 4-6 minutes
d) 10 minutes

4) Give two reasons why sourdough bread is perfect for making French toast. (2)

5) "tang" (line 11). Suggest one synonym and one word which means the opposite. (2)

6) "It's so simple too. The ---1--- to perfect French toast is this: sourdough bread." (line 7). Comment on the sentence structure here and its relevance. (2)

7) What is meant by "hearty crumb of the bread" (line 11)? What is its importance for the final consistency of the bread? (2)

8) Why do you think people don't usually use sourdough bread to make French toast? What bread is commonly used instead? (3)

Writing Task

Create a piece of descriptive writing about your favourite memory. (20)

Marks

Comprehension

Carefully read the passage below and answer ALL of the questions which follow.

Birds 'cry hawk' to give offspring chance to escape predators.

New research has found that the 6 gram brown thornbill mimics the hawk alarm calls of neighbouring species to scare a nest predator by convincing it that a much bigger and scarier predator – the brown goshawk – is on its way. 1

Currawongs, which raid the nests and hunt the chicks of thornbills, are also prey to goshawks. Although currawongs normally benefit from listening in on hawk alarm calls of other species, thornbills exploit this and turn it against them. 5

As well as issuing their own hawk alarm call, thornbills mimic those of the local species to create the impression of an impending hawk attack, which in turn distracts the pied currawong - a predator 40 times larger than the thornbill - providing thornbill nestlings with an opportunity to escape.

While animals often mimic dangerous or toxic species to deter predators, the thornbill is a surprising example of a species mimicking another harmless species to trick a predator. 10

The research, conducted by scientists at the University of Cambridge and the Australian National University (ANU), is published today in the journal Proceedings of the Royal Society B.

"The enormous size difference between a tiny thornbill and a 0.5kg goshawk might make it difficult for thornbills to mimic hawk vocalisations accurately, limiting them to mimicking the chorus of hawk alarm calls given by small local species instead," said Jessica McLachlan, a PhD student from Cambridge's Department of Zoology, who co-authored the study. 15

"As hawks are silent when hunting, the alarm calls of local species may be the only sound that warns of a hawk's presence," she said.

The researchers studied the thornbills and currawongs living in and around the Australian National Botanic Gardens in Canberra. They devised a series of experiments in which they placed stuffed currawongs in front of thornbill nests to test when thornbills use such trickery, followed by experiments testing how currawongs respond to the calls of thornbills. 20

They found that thornbills used their own and mimicked hawk alarm calls when their nests are under attack. They also found that currawongs delayed attacks for twice as long when mimetic and non-mimetic alarm calls were played together as opposed to non-mimetic calls played alone. 25

Marks

"Distracting a currawong attacking the nest could give older thornbill nestlings a chance to escape and hide in the surrounding vegetation," said Dr Branislav Igic from ANU, who led the study.

"It's perhaps the thornbills' best nest defence in this circumstance because physical attacks on the much larger currawong are hopeless," Igic said. 30

Written by Jessica McLachlan / CC 4.0
(http://www.cam.ac.uk/research/news/birds-cry-hawk-to-give-offspring-chance-to-escape-predators)

END OF ARTICLE. Please answer the following questions:

1) How is the thornbill different from other animals which release mimicking cries? (2)

2) Give one similarity and one difference between the thornbill and the goshawk. (2)

3) Why may thornbills mimic the warning cry of other species, rather than simply mimicking the hawk vocalisations themselves? (2)

4) Suggest two synonyms for the word 'mimics' (line 1). (2)

5) What is the advantage of thornbills mimicking hawk alarm calls with respect to the threat by the currawong? (1)

6) Draw a food chain to demonstrate the relationship between thornbills, currawongs and goshawks. Arrows should point from prey to predator. (3)

7) Re-read lines 24-26 ("They also found...played alone.")

   a) Summarise what these lines say. (2)
   b) Why do you think this is the case? (2)

8) Pick an example of an acronym from the text. (1)

9) Why is it crucial for local species that at least one of them releases a hawk warning cry? (2)

10) Why do the thornbills not simply fight with currawongs when under attack? (1)

Writing Task

Do you think the increasing use of technology is making society smarter? (20)

Marks

Comprehension

Carefully read the passage below and answer ALL of the questions which follow.

Why the BBC is wonderfully British

Independent television stations, because of their revenue source, have to appeal to a mainstream audience. The BBC however is more like the NHS, the licence fee being more like a tax, and the wide variety of viewer/listener choice similar to a list of the county's ailments. I think this is a good thing, because it makes the BBC include everyone in their reach. I personally don't have anything against ITV and Five, but I almost never find myself watching them. The adverts are irritating, but the majority of the programmes are not what I consider entertaining. That aside the only programmes I can name (and have watched) on ITV in the last year are Poirot and Marple. These flagship dramas are high quality, and particularly in the case of Poirot represent a long-term investment and not a hastily written script with actors of dubious ability and poor direction, (unlike Van Helsing, for example). 1 5

Channel Four is in a different league to ITV and Five. It buys a lot of programmes from the US, but still has a diverse arsenal of programming - Location, Location, Location and the comic genius of Father Ted and The IT Crowd. Sadly Channel Four is an exception, as has been proved with many years of less successful pay-per-view channels. 10

In terms of radio broadcasts, the BBC holds its own, occupying 4 of the top 5 slots in most listened to radio, with Radio 2 consistently occupying the top slot. This proves that the public are well represented. It is quite reassuring that we pay just shy of 140 pounds per year for a service which is not only incredibly high quality, but also appeals to the vast majority of the population. Admittedly many argue this is a luxury item which should not be hunted down like a tax, but it is a tax that is very cheap. 15

The BBC costs just under £12 per month, whereas Sky is over £30 - and you still have to put up with adverts. 20

Written by Edward Gomez for Dark Matter Sheep / CC 4.0
(http://www.darkmattersheep.uk/blog/why-the-bbc-is-wonderfully-british/)

END OF ARTICLE. Please answer the following questions:

1) Summarise in your own words why the author prefers the BBC to other broadcasting networks such as Channel 4 and Sky. (3)

2) Use the passage to decide which broadcasting channel the following descriptions are about. Options may be used once, more than once, or not at all.

a) Shows programming which represents a long-term investment, and not a hastily written script. (1)
b) Buys lots of programmes from America. (1)
c) Costs at least £1 per day. (1)

Marks

3) Give three synonyms for the word “hastily” (line 8). (3)

4) Give two objections the author has with Channel 5 and ITV. (2)

5) What is the meaning of the word “shy” (line 16) in this context? (1)

6) Re-read lines 10-13. Do you think that the author prefers Channel 4 or ITV programming? Explain. (2)

7) Give one piece of evidence which suggests that the public are satisfied with BBC radio broadcasts. (1)

8) Describe the author’s style of writing. Using evidence from the text, explain why you think he has adopted this style? (5)

Writing Task

Use the picture shown as inspiration for a piece of creative writing. Marks will be given for imaginative descriptions and correct use of vocabulary, punctuation and grammar. (20)

Photo credits to **Alexander Schleicher** / CC 3.0
(https://commons.wikimedia.org/wiki/File:Schleicher_ASH_30_Mi_20110407_130336.JPG)

Mark Schemes & Exemplar Material - Tests 1-15

Comprehension marking criteria and exemplar writing task responses

Instructions for Usage:

> Once you have completed a test, score the comprehension using the mark scheme.
> Refer back to the criteria in the syllabus guide to help mark the writing task.
> There are 40 marks for each test: 20 for the comprehension, 20 for the writing task.
> The exemplar writing task responses should be used for training purposes.
> To monitor progress, use the progress chart and error tally tables.

Marks

Comprehension - Mark Scheme

1) Any three from Indonesia (1), Hungary (1), Tunisia (1) and France. (1)

2) *The student will find this question tricky however it tests the ability to break up words into an understandable phrase within the context of an article.* 'Otherworldly' can be taken to mean as if what it is describing is something remarkable, or otherwise not seen on this earth. (1) Iconography may be further split into 'icon' meaning image/symbol' (1) and 'graphy' meaning study of (not required for mark). As such, we can take this phrase to mean that the images painted on the sides of this pottery are unlike anything we have seen before.

3) Quirky here is used to describe unusual objects which the author owns, such as polka-dotted wine jugs. As such we can take the meaning of quirky to be eccentric, peculiar, unconventional, interesting or weird. (1) An antonym for quirky may be: ordinary, normal, conventional, boring etc. (1)

4) Patience. (1) Fortune is a synonym for luck so this is not correct.

5) Its terroir is ideal, with hot sun for baking (1), clay rich soil (1) and wood for firing. (1)

6) As Christopher Corr lives only an hour's drive from Avignon, we can assume that having the advantage of proximity refers to the benefit of being close (1) to the source of pottery (1) (for the purpose of its collection).

7) The groaning refers to the creaking the wood is making (1) due to the fact that they are so heavily weighed down by his collection of pottery. (1)

8)
   a) True (1) (Barjac is 'about an hour's drive northwest of Avignon')
   b) False (1) ('600 B.C' is around 2600 years ago)
   c) False (1) (I have collected most of my pottery...on shopping expeditions')
   d) False (1) ('Trade with Italy and Spain brought new shapes and coloured glazes')
   e) Can't Tell (1) (He owns a property but we are not told that he lives there)

Writing Task - Exemplar Response

Dear Simon,

I have now been in the satellite for a month, and what an incredible experience it has been. The research I have been sent up here to do is proceeding nicely.
I am allowed to send one letter every month via the shuttle that transports our weekly supplies, though it is known to occasionally fail to reach Earth, so I hope this reaches you.

What a place space is. I peer out of the window to see our planet floating in all its glory. Being up here really puts life into perspective; I can finally comprehend how insignificant we are in the vast cosmos that is the universe. I look down at the tiny smudge on the earth that is the UK, and the even tinier speck of London that sparkles at night like it is a star in the night sky. I sometimes like to wave at you and pretend like you are waving back. When I look out of the other side of the satellite, all I see is an infinite abyss of darkness in which is scattered a countless number of bright, twinkling stars. I wish you, and everyone else back home, could join me on this incredible experience.

It is only me and three other crew members up here – a pilot, engineer and doctor. The craft itself is very cramped. We all share a single bedroom with four beds, accompanied by straps that secure us down so that we don't float away in our sleep. Attached to the bedroom is the bathroom and shower. I say shower, but due to the lack of gravity there is no way for the water to fall down onto our bodies and away into a drain. Therefore, I must moisten towels with water from a bottle, before wiping myself with the wet towels, as if I were receiving a sponge bath. It is moments like these when you take little things like standing under a showerhead for granted!

As I float here weightlessly, my body feels liberated from any kind of shackle. I feel calm, still and at peace, a sensation that even these words don't convey properly. I will be back in five months – until then I am sure time will fly, as I am able to do every day.

Hope to hear back soon,

Avram

Marks

Comprehension - Mark Scheme

1) To make them easier to memorise (1) and repeat orally. (1)

2) One interpretation says that the goal of yoga is to remove fluctuations from the mind (1), whereas the other says that the goal is to abide in one's own true nature. (1) The two are similar in that the latter acknowledges that the prior is the means to achieve the latter. (1)

3) Its texts (Sutras) are very concise to make them easier to memorise (1), and use words which may have more than one meaning (1), also yoga deals with sentient beings which are 'harder to describe and categorise than, for example, chemical elements or geometric entities'. (1) **(quotation not needed to score)**

4) The four modern applications are fitness, meditation, union, and evolution. **(3 marks for 4 correct, 1 mark for 2 or 3 correct, 0 marks for 0 or 1 correct)**
   a) Fitness: The use of postures or powerful practice to realign the body either as prevention or as a cure. (1)
   b) Meditation: Use of breath control and mental concentration techniques to calm and stabilize the mind – the body is used as a tool to gain more control over one's mind. (1)
   c) Union: The use of devotional techniques aimed at joining the inner self with the Universe, sometimes with the added bonus of health and mental benefits too. (1)
   d) Evolution: The idea that Yoga is a practical philosophical system which aims to 'evolve' the practitioner (i.e. increase their internal harmony/connectedness). (1)
   (For each mark, a good proportion of the relevant information in each corresponding passage must be included as a BRIEF summary. Do not award the mark in each case if more than one small piece of information is missing, or if the answers are extensive in length. Max 7 marks awarded)

5)
   a) False (1) ('most practitioners have a personal, unique conception of Yoga that contains some elements of each of the approaches')
   b) True (1) (they 'are seen as secondary effects')
   c) False (1) ('all of these views of Yoga are valid as long as they don't claim to be the only "correct" stance')
   d) Can't Tell (1) (all we know is that some see it as a union between 'one's own internal world and the Universe, Nature or God')
   e) False (1) (it is a 'coherent, systematic discipline in which philosophical concepts and practical methodologies are inextricably linked')

Writing Task - Exemplar Response

All over the world, cows can be seen peacefully grazing in green fields. From a distance, as you travel past the fields they live in, you see them in their herds, standing still as statues. All day long, they stand, just swishing their tufted tails back and forth, back and forth. Up close, you can see them in a whole new light.

Their eyes are huge round pools of liquid gold, gazing aimlessly, framed by luscious black lashes. They stare unblinkingly, betraying no emotion, while their mouths grind slowly in circles on mouthfuls of grass. As they chew, their huge snuffling snouts become covered in green tinged saliva, and you get brief glimpses of their yellow-stained tombstone teeth. Short coarse hairs cover their faces, swirling out in a spiral from the centre of their foreheads. Two ears and two short horns jut out from the sides of their heads.

Their bodies are bulky, and angularly shaped - a white canvas covered in giant splotches of black, like an artist began painting them, and never finished. Four legs, looking almost too small and short, anchor this mass to the ground. They end in hooves that would be shiny black if they were not splattered with mud. Bloated udders, like overstretched water balloons, dangle beneath them.

When cows do decide to move, it is usually to another fresher patch of grass for eating. They move one leg at a time, very deliberately, plodding purposefully for a few metres (until they come to another standstill), swaying side to side gently as they do. Somehow, despite their size, their movement seems to be graceful yet clumsy at the same time.

Every now and again, they call out to each other. A deep lowing 'moo' shatters the air like a foghorn, and one by one the rest of the cows in the herd join in. A brass band, warming up.

Cows are odd creatures, seen everywhere; despite their impressive size, they manage to convey a sense of amiability and peacefullness.

Marks

Comprehension - Mark Scheme

1) The books are the primary learning resource, rather than the teachers, who aren't trained or learned enough to give their own opinion. (1)

2) Textbooks are a way for governments to "instil patriotic values" **(quotation not required for mark)** into its children (1), which it may want to do in order to ensure its citizens will support any future wars the country might have. (1)

3) Publishing companies want to sell as many books as possible. (1) As such they aim to avoid offending the state and local school boards. (1) This results in 'bland' material (1) which often fails to address any controversial aspects about the topic being written about.

4) Avoid/elude/dodge/sidestep etc. (1)

5) Unequivocally/not open for debate/certainly/definitely etc. (1)

6) 1970s textbooks focused less on the tragedies of war and more on numbers and events (1) whereas more recent textbooks have focused more on the human effects of war. (1) 1970s textbooks were "mainly impersonal" (1) OR "paid little attention to the experiences of individual American soldiers" (1), whereas recently the war has been presented in a more negative light (1): "the percentage that presented the Vietnam War as glorious fell from 5% in 1970 to close to 0% in the 1990s" (1) OR "The share of items that present the war as hellish rose from 15% in 1970 to 33% in 2009" (1).
(1 mark for point about 1970s portrayal, 1 mark for sensible quotation, 1 mark for point about recent portrayal, 1 mark for sensible quotation.)

7)
   a) 1970s (1), as this illustrates the nature of war and combat rather than its effects on human life. (1)
   b) 2005 (1), as this illustrates the effects of war on America's soldiers. (1)

8) It may be a reflection on a "growing 'world culture' that values individual persons over the nation or governments". (1) However it may also simply be a response to a "unique military defeat" for the Americans. (1) **(Quotations not required for marks.)**

9) Textbooks still fail to address the effect of war on Vietnamese soldiers and civilians. (1) It is probable that this has been done as it allows textbooks to avoid discussion of the possibility of US guilt for the start or consequences of the war. (1)

Writing Task - Exemplar Response

Dear Diary,

What a day today was – I finally ticked scuba diving in a coral reef off my bucket list. However, following my experience today, I highly doubt that this will be my last time scuba diving.

I closed my eyes as I plunged head-first into the deep turquoise water. I adjusted my facemask so it sat more comfortably on my face. I gracefully kicked my legs, and my flippers effortlessly propelled me deeper towards the carnival of the ocean. Soon, the deep blue of the sea gave way to a visual cacophony of colours. The moment I found myself in the underwater paradise of a coral reef, I knew that this is where I belonged.

Shocking reds, vibrant greens, bright yellows and fiery oranges all sat side by side in this mosaic of nature. Fish of all shapes, sizes and colours smoothly swam as far as the eye could see. Eels cautiously poked their heads out of their holes, before swiftly retreating to safety. A lone, elderly turtle lazily drifted away from the coral reef towards the water surface. A fish panicked by the sight of something as bizarre as a human dove straight into the sea bed, producing a puff of underwater smoke. Anemone gently wafted in the undercurrent, with small families of fish filtering in and out amongst them. Oysters littered the sea bed, and I couldn't help but imagine all the shimmering pearls that lay within them. If my mouth wasn't firmly wrapped around my mouthpiece, I am sure my jaw would have dropped wide open.

When my oxygen tank began to run low, I felt a deep sadness as I was forced to slowly retreat back to the surface, leaving the marine festivities behind me. I clumsily flopped back onto the boat like a fish out of water. I sat on the catamaran as it smoothly sailed back to the shore, my wrinkled feet hanging off the edge. I sit at my desk writing this diary entry, and it makes me miss the water even more. I can't wait to go back, and I'm planning my next trip already!

Olivia

Marks

Comprehension - Mark Scheme

1) A branch fell near a member of staff's tent (1), and so a consultant was called to do a detailed survey of all the trees in the area. (1)

2) Unwind, untangle, disentangle, untwist, straighten out, etc. (1)

3) The first book was implicitly too expensive at £70 (1) and 'Stupsi Explains the Tree' was much more appropriate for beginners in the field as it progresses from simple to more complex ideas in a linear way. (1) This latter book implicitly is the only one of the two that uses cartoons which helps convey complex mechanics and tree biology very accessibly. (1) Furthermore, perhaps the author appreciated that the latter book is a "slim volume" whereas the former book is likely much longer. (1) (Max 2)

4) They are most likely to transport, carry or move water (1), as hosepipes expel water. This is likely why this name has been given. (1)

5) Must assess the time spent under a particular tree (1) as well as the correct identification of the hazard. (1) Assessing time spent under the tree is much easier (1) as anyone can do this, however correctly identifying hazardous trees or branches requires skill, knowledge and practice in this discipline. (1)

6) Lightning. (1) This only comes into play in particular weather conditions which are rare. (1)

7) Accept: someone who looks after/cuts down/tends to trees. (1) One might need to be called if it is thought that there is a chance of a tree falling and or injuring someone in the area. (1)

8) Use of a friendly hedgehog as the main character (1); use of cartoon images so children are not put off by long pages of solid text (1); the book is not too long but is a 'slim volume' so it is not off-putting (1); there is simplified content so that children have more of a chance of understanding it and therefore develop an interest. (1) (Max 3)

9) The study of how living things (bio) (1) work/function/move (mechanics). (1)

Writing Task - Exemplar Response

The ability to play a musical instrument has always been regarded as an exceptional talent. In contrast to many subjects like PE, art, or ICT, it is not something that students are expected to do; learning to play a musical instrument is a subject that must be pursued in your own time. However, it may be that having musical instrument lessons as a compulsory part of the school curriculum would greatly benefit many students.

One argument in favour of compulsory music lessons is that playing an instrument incorporates many different skills; it requires coordination, timing, the ability to read notes, and encourages communication and team work when playing in groups. The ability to produce emotion from a melody on an instrument, requires maturity and creativity. How else does a musician know exactly how long to pause expectantly before tipping into the next flowing phrase of melody? The combination of skills required to play an instrument is an excellent way of learning for many children.

Another argument in favour of everyone learning to play an instrument is that it provides an avenue for some students to excel in, when they are not excelling in other subjects. Over time, more and more emphasis is placed on learning reading, writing and maths. These are undoubtedly important skills, but some students may be more suited to music, and making sure they have the opportunity to discover a natural talent that they possess is important.

Other subjects such as PE and art, which are not considered 'core' subjects are increasingly being offered at schools. There is no reason why music lessons should not also be offered to students, as it provides yet another route for creativity and other skills to be nurtured.

Whilst playing a musical instrument is a valuable talent that some are lucky to possess, it can be argued that it is not a necessary one. Most people get by in life very happily without ever having touched an instrument, so there is no reason that schools should have to provide lessons. If an individual student is interested, then it is an extracurricular activity they can pursue on their own.

In addition to this, music lessons are expensive, due to the fact that they often have to be one on one to be effective. Should schools be spending money on this when there are other essential life skills that can be taught much more cheaply? This is an especially important point if you also consider that many students will not have an interest or aptitude in learning to play an instrument. Money will therefore be wasted where it is not needed or wanted.

In conclusion, I believe that music lessons are an important part of the curriculum due to the wide range of skills it can teach. However, compulsory individual musical instrument lessons is not a practical or beneficial policy. Rather, it would be better for those who are especially interested to pursue it in their own time.

Marks

Comprehension - Mark Scheme

1) King Midas was a friendly and kind man. (1) As Bacchus was a god who adored love (1) he decided to credit King Midas for his generosity.

2) Shouted out, proclaimed, cried out, burst, called, etc. (1)

3) The king was on his knees, praying to the God Bacchus to take back his power (1) as he could no longer eat food or perform common tasks. (1) **(Max 1)**

4)
   a) Any adjective e.g. important, huge, friendly etc. (1)
   b) Any personal pronoun used in the text: e.g. him, her but NOT his/hers (this implies possession) (1)
   c) Any proper noun (i.e. a name, or place), e.g. Bacchus, King Midas. (1)

5) To prance means to dance around (1), which the king was doing as he was happy that his power had been removed, as he could now touch things without them turning to gold. (1)

6) Bacchus is wiser. (1) Bacchus gave King Midas this power in full knowledge that with power comes responsibility, however at first Midas did not know the full consequences of his wish. (1) Bacchus was wise enough to teach Midas a lesson. (1) Bacchus had the knowledge as to how to reverse Midas's wish. (1)
(Max 1 mark for stating that Bacchus is wiser. Max 2 marks for any supportive quote or information from the text. Max 3 marks in total. Max 1 mark in total for counter-arguing that Midas was wiser, provided that a reason is given – e.g. Midas was wise to remember what Bacchus had said and learn from his mistake.)

7)
   a) False (1) ('He bit into a gold nugget instead of the chewy bread.')
   b) Can't tell (1) (this is not stated in the passage)
   c) False (1) ('All you have to do is fully wash yourself in the river')
   d) True (1) ('now all I want is to be normal')
   e) False (1) (both "the piece of steak' and the 'chewy bread' turn to gold)

8) The answer must include the realisations that: the monkey he dreamt about was a representation of himself (1), the cage he dreamt of was this unwanted power he had received which restricted him from living a normal life (1) and the monkey escaping and living happily is linked to the power being lifted from King Midas so he could once again live a free and normal life. (1) Accept the idea that in being represented by 'a monkey', he is portrayed as the less intelligent and more helpless character in the story. (1) **(Max 3)**

Writing Task - Exemplar Response

Winston gripped tightly onto his mother's hand as they elbowed their way through the hustle and bustle of the crowded train station. Adults towered over his small frame, and he squeezed his mother's hand more tightly to prevent himself from being torn from her grasp by the relentless waves of people. The gentle rumble of the stationary train was drowned out by the sound of shouting train conductors and bellowing ticket inspectors. White smoke from the train poured onto the end of the platform, making it look like they were walking into a cloud. The smell of burnt rubber and coal filled the air, causing many people to hold a handkerchief to their noses as they marched along the platform. Winston loved the hubbub of a train station.

A large, portly man with an equally large leather briefcase walked hurriedly past Winston, almost knocking him over in the process having not noticed him, unable to see anything below waist level due to his bulging belly. Winston immediately hugged his mother's waist, seeking some safety from the chaos around him. However, the waist he hugged lacked the softness of the oversized coat that his mother was wearing. He looked up at the perplexed stranger who he was holding. 'Get off me you vagabond!' the unkind lady yelled at him, before pushing him off forcefully using her manicured hand. Where had his mother gone? Winston looked all around him, but was met with a wall of brown coats that obscured his view. He couldn't remember letting go of his mother's hand. Where could she have gone? Why would she leave him alone? Despite there being so many people around him, there was no one to answer his questions. He was lost.

Panicked and with tears streaming down his soft pink cheeks, Winston started shouting 'MUM!' at the top of his lungs, hoping she'd be able to hear her son's cries through the cacophony of the crowd. Minutes passed with no sign of his mother. Losing all hope, he dejectedly walked to the refreshments stand in the hope of buying a cool beverage, before realising he didn't have any money. 'Son, do you want something to drink?' said a familiar, doting voice behind him. He turned around to see his mother standing behind him. He ran at her and jumped up into her arms, tears rolling down his face in joy. 'What on earth are you crying about? I only left to buy us our tickets!' she said, chuckling at Winston's attachment to her. She gently plopped him down on the ground and took his hand once more, before they walked towards their carriage through the hectic crowd.

Marks

Comprehension - Mark Scheme

1) Open-sources helps promote openness/open governance (1), transparency (1), cooperation (1), collaboration/community (1), sharing (1) and digital freedom. (1)
(2 marks for any 3 of the above mentioned, 1 mark for any 2 of the above mentioned.)

2)
a) False (1) ('In his introduction to the book, Trebor Scholz points out')
b) False (1) ('Not all of the essays in this book focus or touch on open source')
c) False (1) ('digital platforms that their users own')
d) Can't Tell (1) (we are not told anything about profitability)
e) False (1) ('The book is more a manifesto than user guide')

3) They need to: make their data flows transparent (1), show where the data about customers and workers are stored (1), show who the data is sold to (1) and show the purpose of storing data (1) (Max 2)

4)
a) Any preposition used: a word used to related a noun to another noun or pronoun (such as above, below, in between, in etc). e.g. "About the platforms and services *on* which those devices and apps rely. (1)
b) Any personal pronoun used: I, you, he/she, we, they. (1) **(Do not accept possession i.e. his, their, etc)**
c) Any conjunction used: a word used to connect two phrases together, e.g. and, but, if etc. (1)

5) The 'open internet' refers to people having full/independent control over their use of internet services (1) and that we should be able to know how big companies use the data that they collect from us. (1) We can tell this as the author complains that "While many of the services that we use are free, we don't have control over them" (1), that the firms "control what we see" (1) "what we hear" (1) and "what we read". The 'open internet' also refers to the idea that big companies must be transparent to us as to how they use the internet data that they collect from us. (1) The author states that these companies "need to show where data about customers and workers are stored, to whom they are sold and for what purpose." (1)
(Max 1 mark for stating that the open internet refers to the user having full control over its use or for stating that it refers to big companies being fully transparent in how they use our internet data. Max 1 mark for a corresponding supportive quotation. Max 2 marks in total.)

6) 'Black-box system of the Snowden-era internet' (1) which suggests that the internet was much like a black-box within an aeroplane, where everything is recorded and monitored (1), which was how the internet was at some point in history, the Snowden era, which indicates the opposite of a transparent society.
(1 mark for quoting any metaphor, 1 mark for appropriate justification as to why it was used. Max 2 marks in total.)

7) *The student will find this question tricky however it tests the ability to break up words into an understandable phrase within the context of an article.* 'Organisations like Creative Commons compensating for the 'privatization of shared intellectual resources.' The article is talking about openness. This is key to understanding this line of text. Privatization may be an unfamiliar word, however, private is the opposite of open, therefore there is something to do with hiding information. The next part is shared intellectual resources. This refers to goods of any sort which lots of people can access that have a unique identifying "intellectual" design property. The phrase therefore means that organisations are restricting open access (1) to uniquely designed goods. (1)

8) Openness and opaqueness are both opposites in meaning. (1) The author has placed these words next to each other to try and highlight the strict contrast (1) about the current 'Opaqueness...of closed systems' compared to his vision of 'promoting openness'. This makes his argument more appealing, and the reader is more likely to adopt his way of thinking, once realising how unfair and problematic the current system seems to be. (1)
(1 mark for any appropriate comment on the author's use of language, 1 mark for suitable analysis of how this language use helps to communicate his point. Max 2 marks in total.)

Marks

Writing Task - Exemplar Response

Dear Diary,

I can't believe that it worked! All friends, family and scientists around me said my time travelling machine wouldn't work, but boy were they wrong!

I stepped out of the capsule into the future world. The first thing I noticed was the smell – there was a strong musk of charcoal, and the air definitely felt thicker, as if you had to drink the air whilst breathing it. The issue with the air became very clear very quickly – everyone wears surgical masks that are clamped firmly around their mouth and nose. Within seconds of stepping out into the open air, a very tall panicked man with a red cross on his shirt clamped one of the devices around my face, immediately freshening the air that I was breathing. I am yet to pinpoint what is exactly wrong with the air.

I walked out onto the street, and to my amazement, I found what looked like cars. Upon closer inspection however, the cars didn't have wheels but instead hovered inches above the ground. Everyone around me was much taller – on average, people appeared to be around six and a half feet tall! Perhaps humans are still indeed evolving. People looked at me as if I was a dwarf!

Not only were humans bigger, but so were the buildings. Skyscrapers extended far above the clouds, with what looked liked flying buses flitting between them as if they were insects flying between trees. While looking up at the skyscrapers, I noticed the sky looked different; clouds looked yellow rather than white, and the sky had a slightly ominous grey tinge to it. The roads appeared to be very generously lit to compensate for this omnipresent darkness. Despite the lack of strong sunlight, it was warm. Actually that is an understatement – it was blisteringly hot. It was winter when I left 2017, so is this what winter is like in 3000? I have so many questions but there is no one to answer them.

Humanity appears to have become much more singular, and much less unique. Everyone was wearing the same coloured shoes that appeared to have a dampening quality, so that every step was made with minimal difficulty. Everyone wore the same rimless spectacles. The most bizarre thing, however, was just how silent everything was. No-one spoke to each other. The hover cars and buses only produced a faint hum as they passed. The dampening shoes ensured that even the characteristic click-clack of stilettos on marble was muffled so that no one could hear them.

'Hello? Can anyone hear me?' I asked those walking on the street around me. Not even a single soul broke their stride. Not a single person looked up at me. Despite the world being seamlessly connected, everyone appeared to be insulated from the activities around them. I don't know how to feel about this new world. It feels very, very lonely.

Dimitrios

Marks

Comprehension - Mark Scheme

1) 28th October. (1) **('Official celebrations begin two days before Diwali')**

2) Row of lights. (1)

3) Putting on or wearing. (1)

4)
   a) Any of: Gold jewellery, fine clothing, sweet treats, household goods (1)
   b) Any of: Padwa, Bhai Duj (1)
   c) Any of: Rangoli, strands of lights (1)

5) Hindus celebrate the triumph of good over evil with higher knowledge being attained and hope overriding despair. (1) This is seen in the text as "Diwali celebrates the victory...oneness of all things." (1) In addition to this, Jains celebrate the attainment of Moksha by Mahavira. (1) This is shown as the text specifies that Jain's celebrate "to mark...Mahavira". (1) Sikhs celebrate Guru Har Gobind Ji freeing himself and the Hindu kings from Fort Gwalior and arriving at the Golden Temple. (1) The text explaining this states that "Sikhs mark the...in Amritsar". (1)
   (3 marks for stating the significances to each of the three faiths, 3 marks for any three suitable corresponding quotations. Max 6 marks in total.)

6) Marks are awarded for spelling, grammar and creative narrative:

   Marks Awarded for Spelling and Grammar
   3 marks: Spelling and grammar almost all correct (allow 1 spelling mistakes/tense mistakes).
   2 marks: Spelling and grammar largely correct (allow 3 spelling mistakes/tense mistakes).
   1 mark: Spelling and grammar allows for comprehension of the story however there are more than 3 spelling mistakes/grammatical errors.
   0 marks: Spelling and grammar impedes clarity of work and the story is incomprehensible.

   Marks Awarded for Creative Narrative
   5 marks: Outstanding creative style, sentence structure and effective use of adjectives, similies and metaphors which show sensitivity to the text and are beyond what can be expected from a candidate.
   4 marks: Excellent creative style, effective use of adjectives, similes, metaphors which incorporates the text style and nouns.
   3 marks: Good creative style with use of at least 2 of the following: adjectives, similes, metaphors and some incorporation of the text.
   2 mark: Some creative style and use of an adjective, similes or metaphor BUT an omission of incorporating the text in some way.
   1 mark: An attempt that may be very brief, highly repetitive, paraphrase the text excessively or have very little relation to the text.
   0 marks: No relation to the text, with incomprehensible phrasing.

Marks

Writing Task - Exemplar Response

Being confined to the school grounds from the hours of 9-3 every weekday can seem an impossibly long time, especially to a child. The possibility of having some freedom during lunchtime, perhaps just for a change of scenery, would be a very attractive proposition to many students, but this is something readily opposed by numerous people for a variety of reasons.

One argument in favour of students being allowed to leave school during lunch is that it allows them more of a break from the drudgery of the school day. By allowing students more free space and variety in their daily activities, they are more likely to come back to school in the afternoon feeling refreshed and ready to learn. The afternoon is always a difficult time for teachers, as the attention of the students' wanes; a proper break from the school environment during lunch time may help prevent this.

Another argument in favour of students being allowed to leave during lunch is that it promotes a life skill that is invaluable in adult life: responsibility. If students were allowed to leave school they would have to be responsible and act appropriately whilst outside, and organise their own time so that they made it back to school on time. Encouraging people to take responsibility from early on would encourage them to consider the accountability of their actions when they are older as well.

However, an opposing viewpoint to this is that it is simply too much responsibility to be placed on children, and that that much trust cannot be given at such a young age. Whilst a student may not mean to do anything wrong, they can be impressionable (especially younger children), and when completely unsupervised by an adult, may be convinced to do silly things.

Furthermore, keeping students inside school arguably creates a more official environment; this reminds children that school is a formal setting for learning to occur, and encourages them to take it more seriously. If schools were viewed by students as a place they could come and go from as they liked, would they not just stop taking it seriously? Some element of formality is needed to ensure students respect their teachers.

In conclusion, I believe that allowing younger children to leave school during lunch break would not benefit their learning. However, older students should be able to be trusted more, and giving them more responsibility over their own lives encourages their independence in a way that is beneficial to their education.

Marks

Comprehension - Mark Scheme

1) 'The day started out ok' (1) 'Well it was a bit boring if I am honest.' (1) 'We got up, got dressed and had breakfast.' (1) ' 'Mum fussed over whether I was warm enough' (1) 'All pretty much normal.' (1) **(Accept any quotations which indicate that the day was originally unremarkable. Max 2 marks in total.)**

2) The dad was afraid his son might catch germs from the gorilla (1), while the mother was afraid he might pass some on to the gorilla himself. (1)

3)
 a) True (1) ('The pride of the zoo is a large silverback called Titan' – later in the passage the term 'silverback gorilla' is used)
 b) False (1) (It had a 'picture of a small deer in the mouth of a large lion')
 c) False (1) ('he was sitting in a hammock strung between two trees')
 d) Can't Tell (1) (we are not told this)
 e) False (1) (it was 'a wide strip of purple carpet')

4) The boy said he was transfixed while he stood watching the gorilla striding around his enclosure, as such we get an idea of the definition of the word: motionless with wonder. (1) Synonyms include: mesmerized, hypnotized, spell bound, captivated etc. (1)

5) E.g. A palace (1) because there were 'ornate chairs and the walls were decorated with silk' (1) and 'the chairs were carved and covered in gold.' (1)
(1 mark for a suggestion of any sensible lavish building or setting, 2 marks for mentioning expensive items or descriptions of the rich environment. Max 3 in total.)

6) **6 marks:** Excellent language (use of well-selected, sensitive language with a very large variety of nouns, verbs, a simile, metaphor, and adjectives). Grammar and Punctuation is flawless. A truly outstanding piece of descriptive writing.
4 marks: Good use of language with a good range of nouns, adjectives, adverbs and at least one simile or metaphor. Punctuation and grammar are very good with only 1-2 minor errors. Overall a good piece of writing.
2 marks: Fair use of language with limited range of nouns, adjectives, adverbs and no similes or metaphors. Punctuation and grammar show recurrent errors.
0 marks: Poor language (a lack of variety of language with only basic use of nouns, verbs and adjectives). Grammar and punctuation is poor, with major errors in tense and phrasing.
(Award 1, 3 or 5 marks if the response appears to fall between the corresponding two sets of criteria)

Writing Task - Exemplar Response

"Wake up, wake up! Come and see!" Lucy's dad cried.

Lucy sleepily opened her eyes to see him excitedly gesturing at the window. Groaning and yawning, she stumbled out of bed, dragging her blanket behind her to go and take a look; with the blanket over her shoulders to protect against the air in her room (which suddenly seemed a lot chillier than usual) she rubbed her eyes and peered out of the window.

Blinding white. For a few seconds, all she could see was bright white light, too bright to tell what was going on. After these few seconds of confusion, her eyes adjusted, and widened with excitement. Everything was covered in a thick blanket of untouched snow. The branches on trees sagged like Dali clocks under its weight, and icicles hung precariously under the window ledges.

Lucy glanced at her dad quickly with a massive grin on her face, and all sleepiness suddenly gone, bounded downstairs to get ready to go outside. Bundled up by her mum in multiple layers with snuggly scarves, knitted woollen hats and countless jumpers, she ran outside, followed closely by her brother and sister. The snow which was previously untouched, an inviting blank canvas, was now trampled and flung around by three sets of eager wellington boots.

All day long they played in the snow: they hurled snowballs at each other; they made snow angels, in patches of untouched snow; they built a huge snowman, dressed in their own hats and scarves; and they slid down steep snowy slopes on plastic bags. They were soaking wet in minutes, their fingers numb from cold and cheeks glowing rosy pink, but they played outside regardless.

Eventually, as it got later, their mum called them back inside. Exhausted, Lucy slumped down by a crackling fire, letting the heat steam off the wet snow that covered her. The heat was more than welcome after the long day outside, and before long her eyes were closing against her own will. At some point, she was carried back up to her own bed. Somewhere, a small sad part of her knew that in the morning there would be no snowy scenes outside the window waiting for her to come and play. That night, however, she slept peacefully, dreaming about the snowy day that she'd had.

Marks

Comprehension - Mark Scheme

1) It indicates struggle, difficulty or a fight to understand. (1)

2) His son was going on a farming camp in Petaluma. (1) Because they were too distracted by the game design to change it to anything more compelling . (1)

3) The author addresses the reader directly making it more personal. (1)

4) A baseball park/pitch/stadium. (1)

5)
   a) Ty Cobb OR Sandy Koufax. (1)
   b) Fifth, sixth, third, fourth (1)
   c) Any adjective used in the text e.g. embarrassing, arcane, professional (1)

6) Any two from: Cardboard, scissors, magic markers, dice. **(Max 2)**

7) Any four from: "turned out to be one of the great educational experiences of my childhood" (1), "It's one of those magical parent-child activities where the two of you occupy shared ground in terms of both comprehension and engagement." (1), "one of those rare experiences that brings out the child in you, and the adult in your child." (1), "how powerful the experience would be as a kind of mental exercise" (1), "Even the simplest game involves layers of creativity and analysis that rival anything your average nine-year-old is doing in school." (1)
   (Accept any other sensible quote in which the author expresses the benefits of building a board game with one's child or in which the author encourages the reader to try it. Max 4 marks in total.)

8)
   a) False (1) ('none of my kids...')
   b) Can't Tell (1) (we are not told)
   c) False (1) ('I've never been one for parenting advice')
   d) False (1) (he hardly played them as he was constantly rewriting the rules)
   e) Can't Tell (1) (there is no information about this)

9) When looking back on a past event/situation. (1)

Writing Task - Exemplar Response

I treaded softly along the cracked concrete floor. The rubber soles of my shoes made no noise as I negotiated the empty paint cans strewn across the ground, tiptoeing tentatively so as to not be heard. I kept my body low to keep my balance steady, like a cat stalking its prey. The sun softly diffused through the dense clouds hanging over the abandoned warehouse, leaving an ominous grey tinge to the sky above.

I had hit the cricket ball over our decrepit fence into the crumbling warehouse next door - the one that my concerned parents always told us not to go into. Although there was no danger to be seen, there was a gloomy ambience in the building that frightened me and filled my actions with caution. I could see my rhubarb-red cricket ball at the far end of the unroofed building, nestled deep in a pile of decaying wood. I'm being unnecessarily anxious, I thought to myself as I finally straightened my back up from my previously stooped posture and began to take long, confident strides towards my ball.

I heard a noise behind me, and sharply turned around. Where did the noise come from? I took another step forward whilst still looking over my shoulder. Before I could take another step, my foot became ensnared by the handle of a bucket that swiftly dragged me straight to the ground. The harsh clang of the metal bucket against the concrete floor echoed throughout the warehouse. Standing up, with the decrescendo of the echo still ringing in my ears, I felt a large hand grasp my shoulder.

I tried to scream but couldn't. The grubby paw pulled back my shoulder, bringing me face to face with a mass of matted, dirty hair through which two piercing blue eyes stared back. The man was clutching a hard morsel of bread in his hand, with a rickety shopping trolley obediently following him closely behind. The unkempt man had a coarse, angular face shaped by a copious coalescence of hair, leaving very little skin visible. His tattered clothes hung loosely from his body, only further enforcing his ghoul-like image in my mind.

With my heart pounding, hands trembling and palms sweating, I ran. I ran as fast as I could. I leapt through the empty window-frame I had clambered in through, sprinted across the unwatered grass surrounding the warehouse, and through the hole in our ramshackle fence. I keeled over, gasping for breath, and looked back at the warehouse. The old man's icy blue eyes gazed back at me. Whilst I expected there to be madness in his eyes, I could only discern desolation. He had my cricket ball in his hand. He threw the ball through the barren warehouse, over the rundown fence, and it rolled to a gentle halt by my muddy shoes. I looked at him puzzlingly, and he returned my stare with a gap-toothed smile. Despite his attempts to smile, I could see the sorrow in his eyes. And before I could say a word of thanks, he turned his back and trudged away out of the warehouse, into the distance.

Marks

Comprehension - Mark Scheme

1)
   a) Shimmering like a diamond (1), like mines. (1)
   b) 'A lone seagull swooped down towards the sea front before climbing back up into the brilliant sky.' (1) (Accept any other quote effectively demonstrating an understanding of the meaning of imagery.)
   c) I looked into the eyes of my trembling son, (1) pounding the ground as she looked up to the heavens (1) (Accept any other quote effectively demonstrating an understanding of the meaning of emotive language.)

2) Unaware, ignorant, etc. (1)

3) Flying his kite. (1)

4) Smooth (1), cooling (1), oblivious. (1) **(Accept any other justifiable adjectives in the correct context of describing the surroundings.)**

5) An ambulance man, police, paramedic. **(Accept anything related. Max 1 mark.)**

6) This suggests that the narrator is not in an ordinary place, and this is unusual. (1) This suggests that the narrator is in danger and that he may have perhaps been hit by a car, or is injured. (1) It is a much shorter sentence than had previously been used (1), changing the mood of the piece. (1) The stationary nature contrasts the high pace ending of the previous paragraph. (1) It is also a stark contrast between the previously talked about boy being wrapped in his mother's towel, an emotive scene, to go on to talk about roads and pavements, a stagnant scene. (1) **(Accept any reasonable comments on the choice of language or structure as to how this sentence contributes to the change in tone. Max 3 marks.)**

7) "Large crowd of people gathering around where I was lying' (1) suggests there is something of interest or drama, and has an effect on the reader of intrigue, as we too want to know what the crowd are looking at. (1) 'Sound of an ambulance' (1) provides further confirmation that this is an injury of some sort, thus warranting the need of the health services, and suggests a sense of urgency, as the ambulance's presence suggests that this is quite a serious injury. (1)
   (Max 2 marks for commenting on how the author creates a sense of drama, Max 2 marks for appropriate corresponding quotations. Max 4 marks in total.)

8) 'Stray pieces of glass, scattered like mines around my body' uses imagery to describe the abundance of hazards, and the use of a simile aids this. (2) 'A cold stream of blood slipped down the side of my cheek'. This describes physical injury and the bringing about of blood is provocative to the reader. 'Man in the jacket anxiously tried along with others to unravel a stretcher'. We trust the man in the jacket because of his profession and even he is anxious. Moreover, he is opening a stretcher which again indicates physical harm. (2) 'Trembling son'. The fear of the son is made evident and emotive. (2) 'Man of the car that hit me, emotionless, his eyes glazed with shock...' The shock of this man also implies that he knows that the consequences of the incident may well be severe. (2)
   (Max 2 marks for commenting on how the author portrays a sense of danger, Max 2 marks for appropriate corresponding quotations. Max 4 marks in total.)

Marks

Writing Task - Exemplar Response

Kai sat on her surfboard, her legs dangling on either side in the crystal-clear water that surrounded the Hawaiian coast. She had been surfing her whole life, and felt more at home on her surfboard than she did on dry land. She bobbed up and down in the waves so that to those on the shore, she could have easily been a buoy. Her wetsuit clung to her tan skin, and her brunette hair had been bleached a lighter shade due to the hours she spent under the sun every day. The salty sea breeze stung her nostrils, but she loved every second of it.

In the distance, she finally spotted what she had been waiting for – the right wave. Years of experience had allowed Kai to read the waves, knowing which one would break at the perfect time. She calmly stroked the water with her right hand, turning her board so that her back faced the waves and she could see the beach straight ahead. Behind her, the perfect wave was fast approaching. She smoothly flopped onto the board so that her sandy stomach pressed against the waxy surface. At the tip of the board, a birthday gift from her late grandfather, her name had been etched in. Kai didn't have to look behind her to know that the wave was approaching – she felt it in her gut. She confidently and powerfully began to paddle with both of her arms, picking up speed so that she could catch the oncoming wave. Behind her, she could feel the tail end of her board begin to rise. A sly grin crept across her face as the wave began to break just behind her.

She began to paddle furiously as the wave grew in size behind her. Most surfers would have attempted to stand up at this point, but Kai had learnt the importance of delayed pleasure, and waited until she reached the crest of the wave before effortlessly crouching on her board. The wind rushed past her head, helpfully pulling her wet hair out of her eyes. Without hesitation, she stood up to her full height. She was as stable and unmovable as a rock once she was on her board. Kai shifted her body weight left and right so that the board cut through the waves like a knife through butter. The longer she rode the wave, the wider her smile grew.

To her right, she saw movement. Her eyes flickered towards the grey mass looming next to her, not daring to move her head for fear of losing her balance. An unmistakable grey fin gradually emerged out of the water, only a few feet away from the board. It was a shark.

Marks

Comprehension - Mark Scheme

1) They are named so because they remain green all year round (1), as they are able to absorb light energy all year round even when it is too cold to photosynthesise. (1)

2) Their leaves still absorb light (1), but as it is so cold they are unable to utilise this energy by photosynthesis. (1) As such they use the xanthophyll cycle (1), where the pigment which usually absorbs light is converted to one which converts light into heat. (1)

3) Dephosphorylation (1), the removal of a phosphate group from a protein. (1)

4) It is most likely aimed at someone with good knowledge in the field (1) due to the use of technical language e.g. "violaxanthin" but with an explanation of what the terms mean (1) e.g. "which absorbs light energy for use in photosynthesis". (1)
(Max 1 mark for correctly identifying the audience, max 1 mark for any appropriate justification from the text, max 1 mark for any supportive corresponding quotation. Max 3 marks in total. If an incorrect audience is chosen with sufficient justification, 1 mark in total can be earned.
N.B. An article aimed at someone with no experience would be much more simple than this, and if aimed at leading experts in the field it would not bother to define the complex language, as it would be assumed that the reader would know what these terms mean.)

5) Periods where the temperature drops and rises (1), causing water/leaves/trees to freeze up and melt out in succession. (1)

6) White spruce. (1) This is the case as "dephosphorylation of light harvesting complexes was faster" (1), meaning it could grow greater and more quickly in spring (1), outcompeting the White pine. Also, with recovery times from winter stress, it was found that "pine took up to three times longer than spruce to recover photosynthetic function" (1)
(1 mark for stating white spruce, max 2 marks for the justifications stated above. Max 3 marks in total.)

7)
   a) False (1) (They looked at 'leaf biochemistry')
   b) False (1) (it rebounds more quickly but because 'dephosphorylation of light harvesting complexes was faster in spruce than pine')
   c) Can't Tell (1) (information not given in the text)
   d) False (1) (can affect function 'over short to long time scales')

Writing Task - Exemplar Response

Ladies and gentlemen, today I am here to speak to you about an incredibly important issue: the devastation that mankind has wreaked upon our planet. Over the centuries, humans have exploited natural resources and dirtied the beauty around us. I hope that today I can enlighten you to this, and that you will leave here with a passion for positive change in our world; positive change that sees the negative effects of mankind lessened.

Humans have scarred the face of our planet in multiple ways. The greed for diamonds, furs, silks, and energy has blinded many people. Blinded them to the effects of their greed on what was once a beautiful planet. Today, deforestation has destroyed exquisite habitats and landscapes, majestic animals have been slaughtered for their skin, and holes have been gauged in the earth in search of expensive stones. Is all of this worth the rewards of diamonds and furs? The atrocities committed by humans for so many years have been ignored for too long.

Besides this, the waste that humans have produced as a result of their greed has contaminated the air, the water and the soil. The air in cities is thick with pollution, sometimes even causing a sooty black smog that people struggle to breathe through. The earth is covered in landfill sites full of rotting rubbish that is being added to faster than the rubbish already present can decompose. The planet's vast oceans, previously a stunning place, now have tonnes of plastic rubbish floating around in them forever, as well as oil and sewage leaks. The effect that this has on the wildlife living in the oceans is also devastating; we are constantly seeing images of green turtles tangled up in plastic like a baby in a swaddling cloth, and seagulls with their feathers stuck together because of sticky black tar.

The result of the pollution that humans have caused is climate change. This adds further to the damage already done, destroying the habitats of creatures, and affecting growth of wildlife. The melting of ice caps all around the world has meant creatures such as polar bears are struggling to survive, whilst also causing sea levels to rise. Climate change also endangers the lives of the human population, causing increasing natural disasters such as fires, floods, and famine.

The cost of humans being on the planet has been great for the Earth. Whilst mankind has contributed many positive changes as well, the devastating effect we have had on the planet for so long is reaching crises point. Real change must happen soon, before the damage we have already caused becomes irreversible.

Thank you all for listening.

Marks

Comprehension - Mark Scheme

1)
- a) Because it meant her artwork either got wet or crumpled. (1)
- b) Because he had glitter on his piece which hadn't dried yet. (1)
- c) The picture he used for superman's face had a beard. (1)
- d) Alice. (1) ""I don't have one of those," Alice said, "or a sister. It's just me and my shadow."" (1)

2) They reasoned that if he left school he would receive an absence mark (1), and that if he played football in the park, people would simply take the ball from him. (1)

3)
- a) She wanted a detachable shadow. (1)
- b) She likely got the idea from the artwork she made or the Peter Pan film (accept either). (1)
- c) She would have someone to talk to (1) and to carry large things/get her homework. (1)

4) Any two from: considered, contemplated, reviewed, thought about, mulled over, reflected on etc. (2)

5) Pick one example of each of the following from the text:
- a) Any used in the text: gingerly, intently etc. (1)
- b) Any used in the text: I, you, we, he/she, him, her, they etc. (1)
- c) Any conjunction in the text: and, as, because, but, for, just as, or, neither, nor, not only, so, whether, yet etc. (1)

6) He made a door hanger with a picture of him on it (1), he was disappointed since he wanted the door hanger "to be better than this" (1), Simon joined the school recently so "didn't really know about Jack and Superman" (1), Jack said: "I just loved everything about him". (1) (Max 3)

7) Her shadow (1)

Writing Task - Exemplar Response

After a long day, the place I look forward to coming back to and feeling safe in is my bed. Nothing beats being able to come back home and snuggle under the duvet with a mug of hot chocolate, a book, and some music.

My bed is a place I have put a lot of effort into making beautiful. It is a double bed covered in a fluffy feather duvet that is patterned with soft pale blue wildflowers. I have piles of plush pillows along the side, in a wide variety of shapes and patterns; these are not only unbelievably comfortable but also look lovely and exciting. The part I am proudest of is the headboard. It's made up of an intricate swirling pattern, covered in a pale satin fabric, and decorated with delicate fabric roses. It manages to give a fairy-like feel to my whole room. Around the walls of my bed I have stuck countless drawings, and photos of friends and family, which have formed a colourful and exotic collage, and this is strung with garlands of fairy lights around it.

Not only does my bed look beautiful, but also it is amazingly comfy! When I lie down, the mattress sculpts around me so it feels like I am easing myself into a warm bath. The duvet is so soft and light it barely feels like it's there, but still feels as snuggly and warm as a hug.

There are a multitude of reasons why my bed is where I feel safest. Firstly, it is the most perfectly cosy environment imaginable. I don't have to worry about anything other than getting into my pyjamas and wrapping myself up tightly in my duvet like a soft cocoon. Having photos of joyful memories, stunning places, and the people I love up around the walls of my bed also mean that when I am there I can be reminded of all these good things; it helps to make the atmosphere in my room even more cosy.

With the soft lighting provided by the fairy lights I think this atmosphere is even more pronounced, meaning that I can never not feel safe as a tortoise under its shell when I am in my bed, snuggled up under the duvet.

Marks

Comprehension - Mark Scheme

1)
1. Answer (1)
2. Balance (1)
3. Sweetness (1) (N.B. though maple syrup may be sticky, this is not balanced out by tang, but sweetness is)
4. Hand (1)
5. Seconds (1)

2) No. (1) They arrived in the evening/dinner time. (1)

3) d) Not 30 seconds as this is how long the whisking process takes. 2-3 minutes is how long the bread is cooked on each side, and 4-6 minutes is the time taken to cook both sides of bread. As such, 10 minutes is the most accurate answer, as extra time will be needed to weigh the ingredients and heat the pan before cooking. (1)

4) It has a slight tang which balances the sweet maple syrup (1), and its texture means it does not go soggy when cooked. (1)

5) As the role of a tangy bread is being questioned in a sweet breakfast, we can assume that tang refers to something which is sour. Synonyms include: sour, sharp, zesty, bitter etc. (1) An antonym would be: sweet. (1)

6) This line is made of three short, simple phrases. (1) This mimics the fact that it is telling us the simple secret behind perfect French toast. (1) The use of a colon makes it instructive, hence the author effectively convinces the reader of the best approach. (1) (Max 2)

7) 'Hearty crumb of the bread' is a description of the bread's firm/dense texture (1), which means that the bread does not turn soggy when fried. (1)

8) Sourdough is –as its name suggests- a fairly sour loaf. (1) As such it is more often used with steak and other savoury dishes than it is with desserts or sweet breakfasts as the flavours may be assumed not to match for the latter. (1) Also, the value of using sourdough for French toast is implicitly not well known – that is, it is not widely publicised (1) White bread is usually used. (1)
(Max 2 marks for points above related to why people don't usually use sourdough bread for this purpose, 1 mark for stating that white bread is usually used. Max 3 marks in total.)

Writing Task - Exemplar Response

My favourite memory is the day I built myself a small boat at my grandparents' house in India, when I was eight years old. I woke up that morning searching for an activity to do, as I had spent many days lazily curled up on the veranda reading books. In search of inspiration, I decided to take a walk through the coconut plantation that lay adjacent to our house. Walking through the leaf litter and unkempt grass, I came across the creek I had swum in since I was a young boy. In that moment a light bulb switched on in my head, and I decided to build a boat.

I went into my grandfather's workshop and pilfered all of his rope. I additionally tried to take a hammer and some rusty nails, but my grandfather snatched them out of my hand before I could go any further. Regardless, with fraying rope in hand, I walked out into the dense thicket that was the plantation in search of some materials to build my boat. An hour later, proudly drenched in sweat and mud, I had collected all the materials I could find: three large pieces of bamboo that would serve as my primary floatation devices, and various branches I hoped to lash between the pieces of bamboo to serve as a platform to sit on.

I cut the extremely lengthy piece of rope into metre-long pieces, which I used to tie together all the wood I found in an unplanned, untrained and messy manner. Regardless, all the pieces of wood held together, and my makeshift boat, perhaps more aptly described as a buoyant platform, was ready. With the help of my grandfather, I carefully carried it to the creek, where I gently set it down onto the remarkably still water. To my amazement, it floated! I kicked off my sandals into the mud, and cautiously climbed onto my boat, which easily held my small frame. And there on that boat I spent the rest of the day – like a prince, I demanded that my lunch was brought to me on my boat, and book in hand I remained there for the rest of the day. That boat, which I had built all by myself, provided me with an immeasurable sense of achievement and happiness at the time, which is why that day is my favourite memory.

Marks

Comprehension - Mark Scheme

1) Most other animals which mimic other species will mimic ones which are perceived as dangerous or toxic. (1) The thornbill on the other hand mimics another harmless species (1), allowing its nestlings time to flee.

2) Similarity: Both brown (1) Differences: Vastly different weight, different vocalisations, one is prey with the other being its predator. (1)

3) It is unable to do so (1), as the thornbill may be too small to produce these kinds of sounds accurately. (1)

4) Any two of: Mime, mirror, copy, simulate, resemble, echo, parrot, act, impersonate etc. (2)

5) This distracts the currawong if it is attacking the thornbill, giving the thornbill time to escape. (1)

6) 1 mark for both the arrow from the thornbill to the currawong and the arrow from the thornbill to the goshawk. (1) 1 mark for the arrow from the currawong to the goshawk. (1) 1 mark for all arrows pointing in the correct direction with no extra arrows. (1)

7)
   a) This says that when currawongs hear both the hawk cries of other tiny animals as well as the thornbills', they wait twice as long before attacking thornbill nests (1) compared to if they hear only the thornbill's. (1)
   b) This is likely because when the currawongs hear the mimicked cries of other small animals, they fear that a larger predator, the goshawk, may be in the area (1) and therefore the currawongs themselves hesitate to enter the area because of the risk of being attacked themselves. (1) They may alternatively be waiting for the goshawk to leave (1) or they may expend extra time looking out for goshawks. (1) (Max 2)

8) ANU (1) - (do not accept Australian National University), PhD (1) - (do not accept Doctor of Philosophy). (Max 1 mark. N.B. acronyms may use the first few letters of the component words, not always just the initials.)

9) Hawks hunt in silence (1), so without one of these warning cries no one would know it was coming until it was too late. (1)

10) Currawongs are 40 times the size of thornbills, so the thornbills would almost certainly be killed. (1)

Marks

Writing Task - Exemplar Response

Society is constantly advancing, finding ways to make people's lives easier and more efficient. The increasing use of technology plays a big role in this in the following ways: allowing easy access to information at all times; reducing the amount of time it takes to perform certain tasks; and enabling easy communication between people all over the world. However, has technology closed as many doors as it has opened?

There are many strong arguments in favour of the argument that technology is making us smarter. The ability to share information from around the world over the internet, and the ease with which this information can be accessed allows people extraordinary amounts of knowledge they may never have been exposed to growing up 100 years ago. Whereas without the internet, books and newspapers would have had to be relied upon to provide all the information you needed, a quick internet search now could provide all the information needed, and more. With such ready access to a multitude of facts, how could technology not be making society smarter?

Furthermore, the sheer enormity of the amount of information available on the internet means that to find the relevant information you need becomes a skill in itself. The skill of deciding which information is reliable or trustworthy encourages a new way of thinking about the facts that are being presented; this also helps make society smarter in a different way.

Another point is that many technologies (such as cars, computers or microwaves) reduce the amount of time taken to perform daily chores, leaving more time available for learning. Without these technologies, more time would be spent cooking, cleaning and travelling, allowing less time for people to sit down and learn about something that they are interested in.

However, there are also many disadvantages to the increasing use of technology. One argument is that technology in fact makes society lazier. As all facts are so easily found, it reduces the need to learn them. There has been a shift from learning to solve complex problems yourself, such as complex maths equations, to just using technology to solve it for you. Whereas in the past information must be found by reading a wide variety of books, now you can copy and paste a paragraph off of Wikipedia.

Furthermore, this shift from reading a wide range of books to find the information you need, to just finding a paragraph, has limited the range of knowledge that people are exposed to. Reading a whole book on a subject gives a more general overview of a subject than merely reading a few facts will. Therefore, technology may be helping society find specific facts, but it allows people to overlook the bigger picture, thereby making them less smart.

In conclusion, I believe that technology has made society smarter. The extraordinary access to vast amounts of information, and the ability to communicate and share this information with people all over the world is amazing. However, society must be sure to use the technology in the right way, and not overlook the values of other sources of information.

Marks

Comprehension - Mark Scheme

1) A variety of shows for everyone ('BBC include everyone in their reach', 'wide variety of viewer/listener choice similar to a list of the county's ailments') (1), the public is well represented on radio (BBC hold its own occupying 4 of the top 5 slots in most listened to radio). (1) No irritating adverts like ITV or Five ('adverts are irritating') (1), not entertaining ('the majority of the programmes are not what I consider entertaining.'). (1) The cost is reasonable; Sky costs over £30 a month and still has adverts, whereas BBC is just under £12, ('The BBC however is more like the NHS, the licence fee being more like a tax.') (1) **(Max 3 marks in total. Quotations not necessary.)**

2)
   a) ITV (1)
   b) 4 (1)
   c) Sky (1)

3) Rushed, hurriedly, briskly, quickly, speedily, rapidly. **(Max 3)**

4) According to the author, the 'Adverts are irritating' (1), the 'majority of programmes are not what I consider entertaining' (1) and 'Channel Four is in a different league to ITV and Five' (1) It is also implied that the latter two of these have a less "diverse arsenal of programming' compared to Channel Four. (1) **(Max 2)**

5) Just short of the amount i.e. almost at the amount, but not quite there. **(1 mark. N.B. The most common use of shy - 'nervous' or 'timid' - is not applicable here, as the less common informal definition is the one relevant to the context.)**

6) Channel 4 (1), as the tone adopted for Channel 4 is positive 'Channel Four is in a different league', and 'comic genius' suggests the author approves of the Channel's shows. (1) The opposite arguments are also applicable: In contrast Channel 5 is described as with 'the majority of programmes are not what I consider entertaining.' (1) 'The only programmes I can name on ITV' suggests the author himself does not know many programmes on ITV, and therefore has little interest in the channel. (1)
(1 mark for stating 'Channel 4', 1 mark for any one piece of supportive evidence stated above. Max 2 marks in total.)

7) BBC holds its own occupying the 4 of the top 5 slots in most listened to radio. (1) Radio 2 consistently occupies the top slot. (1) **(Max 1 mark)**

8) The style is very opinionated (1), therefore a lot of his writing is about what he feels and thinks (1), and sometimes is a bit extreme, '4 of the top 5 slots in most listened to radio... proves public are well represented'. (1) 'Prove' is a strong word in this context (1) and so demonstrably the author feels strongly about his views with the intention of convincing the reader of his side of the argument. (1) His tone is assertive (1), with further evidence of this through statements such as 'I think this is a good idea (1) and the stark contrast in his opinion of Channel Four being in 'a different league to ITV and Five'. (1) His style is also very informative (1), as his listing of several shows implies that he is an expert on the topic and so his opinion should be trusted. (1)
(Max 3 marks for listing stylistic choices, Max 3 marks for analysing the author's reasons for choosing the mentioned styles with evidence. Max 5 marks in total.)

Marks

Writing Task - Exemplar Response

Ramy peered cautiously out of the crystal-clear glass. Until this moment he'd lain slumped in his chair, looking timidly at his feet rather than out of the glider plane, flying at 5000 ft.

What met his hazel eyes was the most breathtakingly astonishing view that had ever been bestowed upon him. The mountains stood majestically in the distance, looking over the populous valley that lay below. Cars driving along roads looked like ants crawling hurriedly towards their home. The alternating wheat and grass fields below resembled a quilt stitched together by mankind that had been laid across the ground to keep it warm. He felt like he was walking on air.

The silence of the engineless glider provided Ramy with a sense of peace and calm he had never experienced before. He looked to his left and right; the slender white wings of the glider extended far out on either side, making Ramy feel like he was an albatross. The plane rose up and down alongside the thermal currents. In the far distance, he could see the runway approaching. The pilot gently turned the plane to the left, and the glider serenely swooped as if it were circling prey. Time seems to move slowly, thought Ramy to himself, as fast-moving trains appeared to trundle slowly across the massive landscape as if he was viewing life in a time-lapse. As the glider neared the runway, life began to resume at the pace he was more familiar with. Pigeons violently veered out of the way of this new, dominant bird that now occupied their air space.

The glider effortlessly kissed the hot tarmac as it touched down, landing delicately as if even the slightest contact would shatter the plane into a thousand pieces. Ramy lifted the dome-shaped window above his head whilst the plane rolled gently to a halt. The breeze gently wafted through his chestnut-coloured hair, and the unmistakable scent of the freshly-cut grass filled his nose.

Ramy landed onto the asphalt with a dull thud as he jumped off the plane, his mind completely numb, as if he had just been separated from the reality of the world. For the first time in his life, he felt at peace.

Progress Chart

After marking each English test, find where your child's test score meets the upwards arrow of the corresponding test, and draw a cross. You can find out what estimated percentage of candidates would achieve a lower score by reading off the percentile values to the right for each test. To better spot the trend of how your child is progressing in terms of test scores and percentiles, connect successive crosses with straight lines. Underneath the chart, you can write down the scores and percentiles successively so that you can quickly look back on them later.

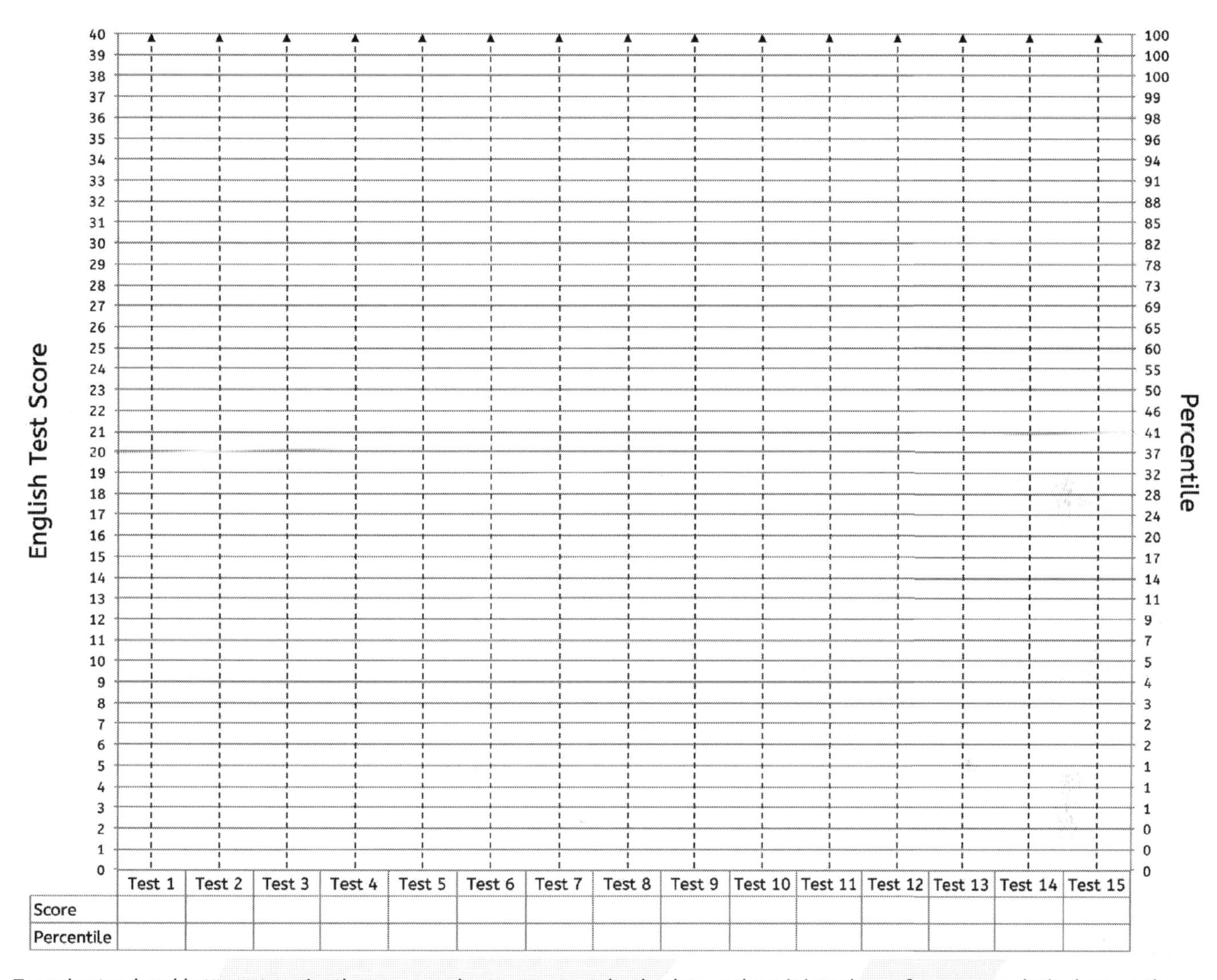

	Test 1	Test 2	Test 3	Test 4	Test 5	Test 6	Test 7	Test 8	Test 9	Test 10	Test 11	Test 12	Test 13	Test 14	Test 15
Score															
Percentile															

To understand and better categorise the progress charts, you can take the data and put it into the performance analysis chart on the next page. This chart allows you to develop a grading system to better study the scores that your child is getting.

We understand the value of being able to closely record and monitor your child's progress - indeed, many parents build rewards systems around them to help get their children into a steady work ethic. However, it is important that your child does not get disheartened if they do not score the mark they wanted. It is likely that as they become more familiar with the syllabus, they will achieve higher and higher marks. The purpose of this chart is for you to understand what rough level your child is at now, and to build targets around it.

On the contrary, if your child is scoring very highly, then these progress charts should provide some strong reassurance. It is important that your child keeps working through the tests to ensure that their level doesn't drop. Moreover, you may want to start thinking about scholarship programmes and raising your child's targets in accordance with these. We have intentionally included some scholarship-standard questions in every test that are of very high difficulty. It is therefore extremely uncommon that a child scores 100% in a test. We like to make sure that our papers push candidates at every level.

To build these charts, we ran trial tests around the UK and accumulated data from several students who were all due to sit independent school exams within the next 12 months. We corresponded the different scores that students were getting to the percentile that they fell within. It is important to note that while your child's scores climb, the percentile increase will follow a different pattern. Gaining 5 marks with a baseline score of 20/40 corresponds to a percentile climb of 23%, whereas with a baseline score of 35/40 the percentile climb is only 4%. It becomes harder and harder to climb those last few percentiles!

Performance Analysis Graphs and Grading

Use the graphs to analyse your child's performance. Simply take their score in any test, and read off the percentile to find out how your child did compared to others. Please note that since our tests vary in difficultly slightly, and since these graphs are estimates across all of our tests, you should take slight changes in performance lightly. It is possible for you to read off the percentiles using the progress chart on the previous page alone, but this graph makes it more clear visually how student scores are spread out. The table below the graph explains how you can grade each paper, and is colour co-ordinated with the graph.

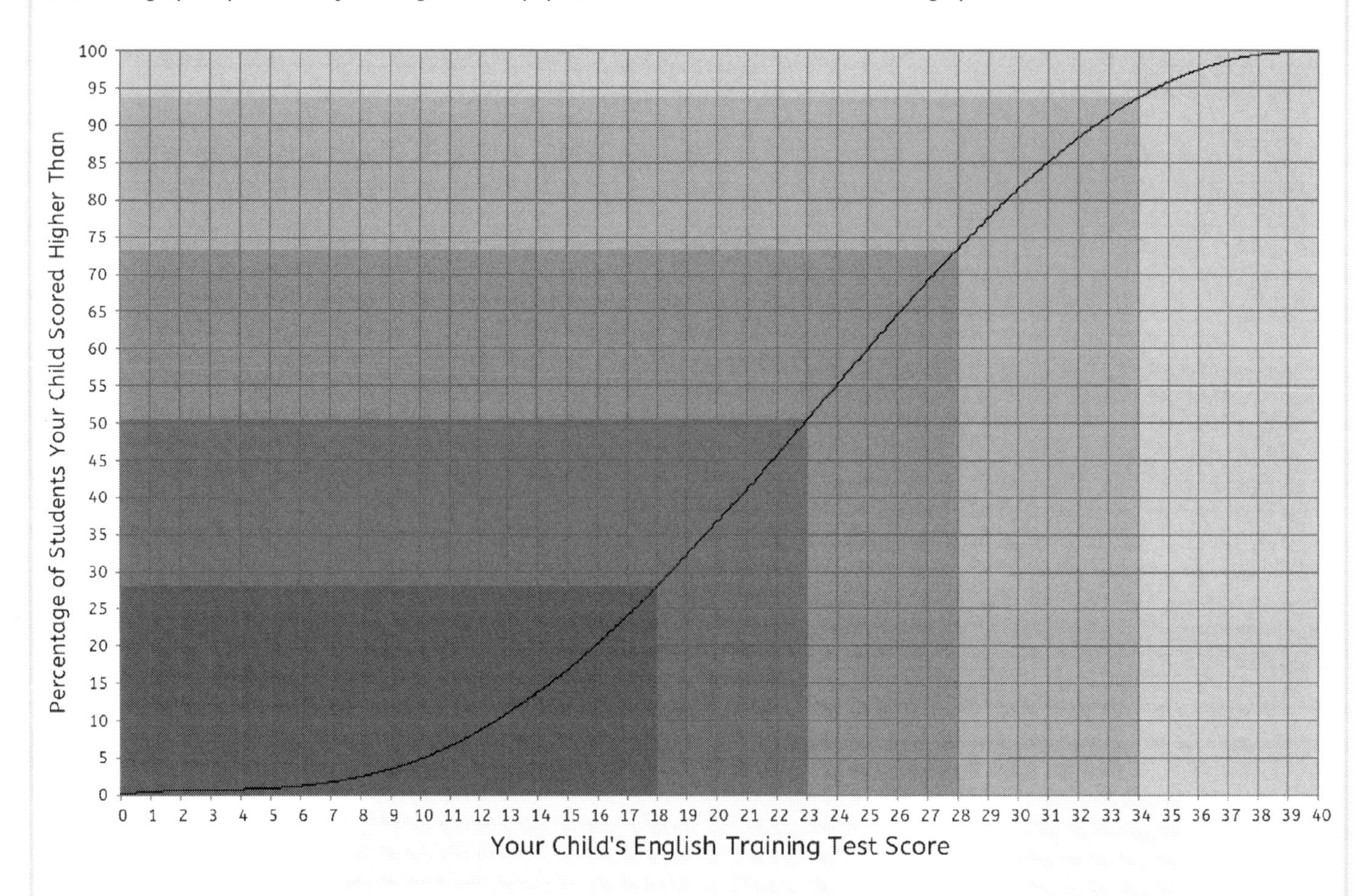

English Score	Grade
35-40	Outstanding
29-34	Excellent
24-28	Satisfactory
19-23	Coasting
0-18	Improvement Needed

English papers are usually quite hard to mark, particularly on opinionative questions. However, our papers come with the most rigorous exemplar mark schemes on the market, and so it is very possible to narrow down on a definitive score.

Children should focus on developing their vocabulary and ensure that they use grammar that they are familiar with, as well as enriching their work with linguistic tools. A good way to work on these qualities along with improving creativity is to encourage your child to read lots of fiction books.

You may find this grading system useful in building up more specific reward systems for your child. Please remember that this data was collected from a large number of students who were within 12 months of sitting their Independent School 11+ examinations. We understand that some parents give their children our resources a little early, in order to get ahead of the rest of the cohort. In these contexts, the grading system may be less appropriate for them. The person who knows your child the best is you, and if these targets don't work for you, then we recommend that you change them to suit your needs.

If your child is scoring 0-18, we recommend strongly that you cover content with them before they attempt further tests. It means that there is a good chance that they are not ready to sit the tests just yet - sitting repeated tests in such a case will not build up their knowledge of first principles. At Secondary Entrance, we offer a holistic set of services, and so if you feel that your child needs help with learning the concepts, please feel free to turn to our In-Person and Skype tuition services.

If your child is scoring 35-40, their mark is outstanding. This means that they are performing extremely highly and you may want to begin thinking about scholarship training. Again, our In-Person and Skype tuition services can help you with this if you wish.

Tally Tables

After marking each English test, you can refer back to the walkthrough and see which types of question your child is getting wrong. You can record errors here, and figure out which areas they need to work on the most.

Comprehension Styles:

Record your child's overall comprehension scores here and see how they fare with different styles of article.

	TEST 1	TEST 2	TEST 3	TEST 4	TEST 5	TEST 6	TEST 7	TEST 8	TEST 9	TEST 10	TEST 11	TEST 12	TEST 13	TEST 14	TEST 15	TOTAL
BOOK EXCERPTS																
SCIENCE JOURNALS																
NEWSPAPER ARTICLES																
BLOGS																
INSTRUCTION-BASED TEXT																

Comprehension Question Types:

Record your child's individual scores for various question types here to see what their strengths and weaknesses are.

	TEST 1	TEST 2	TEST 3	TEST 4	TEST 5	TEST 6	TEST 7	TEST 8	TEST 9	TEST 10	TEST 11	TEST 12	TEST 13	TEST 14	TEST 15	TOTAL
GRAMMATICAL ANALYSIS QUESTIONS																
TEXT ANALYSIS QUESTIONS																
OPINION-BASED QUESTIONS																
OTHER																

Writing Task Styles:

Record your child's overall writing task scores here and see how they fare with different question styles.

	TEST 1	TEST 2	TEST 3	TEST 4	TEST 5	TEST 6	TEST 7	TEST 8	TEST 9	TEST 10	TEST 11	TEST 12	TEST 13	TEST 14	TEST 15	TOTAL
DESCRIBING AN EXPERIENCE																
PICTURE DESCRIPTION																
BOOK REVIEW																
ARGUMENTS FOR AND AGAINST A CASE																
CREATIVE WRITING																
OTHER																

Writing Task Criteria:

Record your child's individual scores for the specific marking criteria to see where they are gaining and losing marks.

	TEST 1	TEST 2	TEST 3	TEST 4	TEST 5	TEST 6	TEST 7	TEST 8	TEST 9	TEST 10	TEST 11	TEST 12	TEST 13	TEST 14	TEST 15	TOTAL
PLANNING (OUT OF 3)																
STRUCTURE (OUT OF 3)																
SPELLING AND GRAMMAR (OUT OF 5)																
LANGUAGE (OUT OF 4)																
CONTENT / STORY (OUT OF 5)																

Some children are very creative, whereas others have their strengths in being attentive to detail, and others are meticulous in their spelling and grammar. These differences mean that every student gains and loses marks in different areas. English papers require a lot of sifting through information and involve a lot of writing - they are some of the most tiring. It is only healthy for a child to work a limited number of hours in a day and so it is important that they focus on weak areas in order to make best use of their time.

Healthy Learning Tips

11+ revision can get intense, particularly when close to the exams. It is crucial to supplement learning with a routine that consists of sufficient exercise, outdoor activity, proper diet and ample sleep, in order to stay efficient and healthy.

Can Work Become a Hobby?

How to revise without sitting at a desk

At Secondary Entrance, we truly believe in the term 'work hard play hard'. We wouldn't want your child to sit and revise abstract concepts without understanding the real life context. Sometimes it is not completely clear to a child why they may be working so hard on 11+ test papers and revising. Often it is in their benefit that they do not, to avoid unnecessary stress nearer to an exam. As an 11+ parent, being immersed within the learning process as much as your child is fundamental to their learning.

Foster a love for learning

Doing 11+ practice papers can be boring. We know because we ourselves remember all those years ago revising for our very own 11+ exams, and wanted to play outside or watch TV, not sit at a desk and do past papers. However, learning is at its best when you or your child are not aware of it, or better yet, when you are both enjoying it. By providing a learning environment that is ever-changing and engaging, learning can move outside of answering questions. Examples of this include going into the garden and counting flowers or spotting animals.

How can I Create a Structured and Varied Learning Environment?

Have something to look forward to, every time

When your child is about to start a paper, give them something to look forward to once they complete it, such as a snack, or time playing their favourite game. Having this ensures that work is not associated with unhappy thoughts, and instead is a journey, with a prize at the end of it.

Spread out the learning process in small, bite-sized chunks

A child's brain is amazing! It is able to absorb vast amount of information, more so than adults, and can learn at a very rapid rate. However, this rapid level of learning also requires regular breaks and plenty of nourishment. It is unrealistic to expect your child to work for more than an hour at a time. Create big breaks in between tests, to allow their brains lots of time to consolidate their learning.

Take learning outside of the study room!

Try going to the local park or museum! Challenge your child in new ways, such as creating maths problems using sticks or stones in the park. By making learning an engaging activity, children are more likely to retain information and are less likely to avoid working. Topics like non-verbal reasoning simply require pattern recognition, therefore spotting patterns in the environment is still learning but in a less obvious way than direct mathematics, for example. Being active within the learning process as a parent gives a child further reason to want to work. They go through this as part of a team. Leading by example is an effective means of teaching healthy learning habits.

Physical exercise is just as important as mental exercise!

It is vital that whilst you exercise your mind, you also exercise your body. Ensuring your child engages in activity every day is so important to their well-being, and also ensures that they feel fresh and energised when they do work. Whether this is swimming, running, playing in the park or football, exercise of any sort is as important as working!

Sleep!

Whilst your child works during the day, it is also important to avoid working too late at night, and that they have at least 8 hours of sleep a night. Sleep is such a valuable part of the revision process, helping the brain to filter through the information of the day, build new connections and organise it for quick retrieval at a later date. A child that is well rested will get more from a revision session than one that is sleep deprived, thus this should not be overlooked.

How can I Improve my Child's Learning Outside of School?

<u>Going to museums</u>

Museums are a brilliant way of bringing science, history and the arts to life. They have a lot of fun interactive exhibits to keep children entertained, but to also educate them on the fundamentals of science and art. By seeing important artefacts and demonstrations, children begin to understand the real-life applications of what they have studied.

<u>Shopping with your child</u>

Whilst this may simply be grocery shopping, getting them to calculate the price of the items in your basket is great for mental maths and can make any shopping trip exciting! You could also ask them to work out the price of a product after a discount, or how much you could save in your basket with 2 for 1 deals considered.

<u>Travelling</u>

Perhaps your child could assist you in planning a route, or finding the fastest way of getting around town. Giving them real world problems with an incentive is fun and engaging, and helps develop problem solving abilities! If in London they could plan a tube route, or if in a car they could work out how long it will take to get to your destination if you give them the distance and speed you are travelling at.

<u>Spelling games whilst reading the newspaper</u>

Newspapers are a great place to find fun little puzzles, such as crosswords and Sudokus. You may also be able to find a number of new words that your child has never encountered before, and be able to teach them what they mean in the process. Moreover, secondary schools that interview often like to ask about what your child may have seen in the news, and so you can keep them current on events that are happening in the world.

<u>Playing board games such as Pictionary or Scrabble!</u>

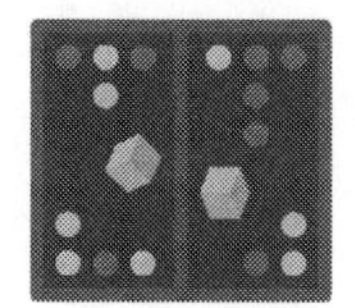

Scrabble is an effective means of improving a child's vocabulary in a relaxed and fun environment! It challenges them to sift through all their current vocabulary, but also to run to the dictionary to find new words! They will continually question whether certain combinations of letters make a word or not. This truly is verbal reasoning in action! Pictionary improves their visual and perceptive skills, and so may indirectly help them with maths and non-verbal reasoning. It does so in a fun way where the emphasis is on drawing and earning points.

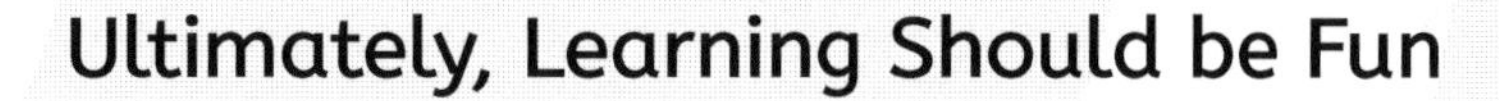

Ultimately, Learning Should be Fun

<u>Try to find learning resources that your child enjoys using</u>

Whilst at Secondary Entrance we want your child to achieve the best they possibly can, it must be remembered that they are still developing socially, physically and mentally. Giving them the widest possible number of experiences and exposure to different activities is at the core of fostering life-long learning. For them to develop their own reasoning of situations is the ultimate goal of all of our papers. Our aim has been to design our resources in a way that provides long-term as well as short-term benefits to your child. We welcome any feedback about your own personal thoughts on education, as we too are also learning, and want to offer the best possible products to our clients!

How to Prepare for the 11+ Exams

At Secondary Entrance, we have all done exams. A lot of them. The majority of our staff are continually being assessed even now, and so our understanding of exams goes far beyond just being academically prepared for them.

12 months before the exam:

You and your child should familiarise yourself with the exam style for whichever exam your child will be sitting. You should try and find the appropriate syllabuses if they exist, or look at existing materials on the school's website to get a general idea of what is tested.

It is also worth keeping an eye on how your child is doing at school at this stage, and try to develop a good idea of their strengths and weaknesses. With this knowledge, you should aim to fill out any gaps in their knowledge. How can Secondary Entrance help? Within each of our 11+ practice papers, a large range of syllabus points are accounted for. In this way, you can identify the knowledge gaps early on and work smart.

Your child should attempt practice papers to get used to doing exams. This should be in a non-pressured environment, with plenty of time to read, internalise and ponder over every question. They should do no more than one paper a day, and should rotate papers to keep it mixed.

6 months before the exam:

Your child should be quite well rehearsed with the idea of taking practice papers in a relaxed environment by this stage. You may now attempt to time the papers, as per the recommendations at the front of the practice packs.

It may be that your child does not finish the paper, or that they rush near the end and miss some easy marks. These sorts of mistakes are important to make, as they will teach your child exam technique. They will learn naturally that missing out long-winded questions and revisiting them later may make sense if they are only worth one mark. Remember that getting your child into the habit of doing timed papers reduces stress closer to the exam, as they are familiar with what they will ultimately have to do.

3 months before the exam:

The number of papers your child is doing can increase up to a maximum of 2-3 per day at this point. Their timing should now be more up to speed, and you can experiment with targets to help them increase their marks further if you find that they are starting to plateau.

If your child starts to tire, or begins to adopt rout learning routines, this is often an indication that things need to be mixed up a little bit. Visit our healthy learning advice to see the variety of learning approaches that you may wish to try out.

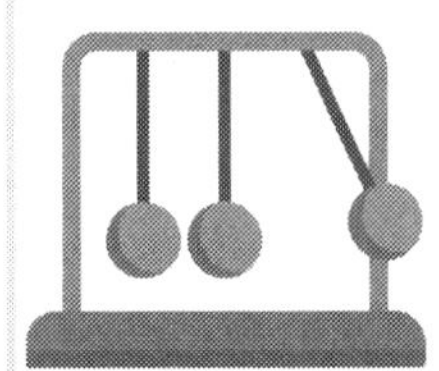

1 month before the exam:

11+ exam technique is now the focus. It may help, even if only for a short period of time, to recruit a tutor who can run through technique tips with your child. A tutor can also help at this stage with topics which are proving to be a persistent problem.

The other benefit that having a tutor or otherwise constantly working with your child can have is taking care of nerves. With such little time coming up to the exam, it is normal for some panic to surface. Having a tutor can help reassure you that a professional is taking care of your child's immediate academic needs.

1 week before the exam:

At this point, most of the preparation for the 11+ should be complete, and most of your Secondary Entrance papers should be completed. Some final practice using past papers that the schools may offer on their website may help keep your child's mind freshly targeted to the specific material that they are about to encounter.

You must remember that most of the preparation at this point is complete, and that rest and leisure remain very important. Cramming hundreds of papers into this week is not an effective means of preparation, and leads to anxiety and fatigue.

The day of the exam:

All the preparation is now complete. You and your child are as prepared as they ever could be for the 11+ exam papers, and your child should have nothing to worry about. They should know what to expect for the exam, and if there is a question that they cannot do, they have adequate preparation to keep them calm and help them have as good a shot as possible.

With the help of adequate advice, tutoring and high quality preparation material, hopefully Secondary Entrance has been able to unload much of the stress for both you and your child.

Revision Timetables

A little a day goes a long way. Equally, it is important for your child not to wear themselves out by working too hard, too soon. Our revision schedules are sensible, effective and integrate healthy supplements to your child's learning.

12 Months Before the Exams

We recommend this schedule for those with a year to go before their exam - it is not too intense at all. It covers three tests in a week, and 'break-days' have a single slot to mark the previous day's paper and go over any incorrect answers.

Monday	Tuesday	Wednesday	Thursday	Friday	Saturday	Sunday
Day 1 Maths - Test 1: *60 Minutes*	Day 2 Maths - Review: *25 Minutes*	Day 3 English - Test 1: *70 Minutes*	Day 4 English - Review: *25 Minutes*	Day 5 Verbal - Test 1: *40 Minutes*	Day 6 Verbal - Review: *25 Minutes*	Day 7 Break: *Full Day*
Day 8 Non-Verbal - Test 1: *60 Minutes*	Day 9 Non-Verbal - Review: *25 Minutes*	Day 10 Maths - Test 2: *60 Minutes*	Day 11 Maths - Review: *25 Minutes*	Day 12 English - Test 2: *70 Minutes*	Day 13 English - Review: *25 Minutes*	Day 14 Break: *Full Day*
Day 15 Verbal - Test 2: *40 Minutes*	Day 16 Verbal - Review: *25 Minutes*	Day 17 Non-Verbal - Test 2: *60 Minutes*	Day 18 Non-Verbal - Review: *25 Minutes*	Day 19 Maths - Test 3: *60 Minutes*	Day 20 Maths - Review: *25 Minutes*	Day 21 Break: *Full Day*
Day 22 English - Test 3: *70 Minutes*	Day 23 English - Review: *25 Minutes*	Day 24 Verbal - Test 3: *40 Minutes*	Day 25 Verbal - Review: *25 Minutes*	Day 26 Non-Verbal - Test 3: *60 Minutes*	Day 27 Non-Verbal - Review: *25 Minutes*	Day 28 Break: *Full Day*
Day 29 Maths - Test 4: *60 Minutes*	Day 30 Maths - Review: *25 Minutes*	Day 31 English - Test 4: *70 Minutes*	And So On...			

Review- look back

The 31-Day Revision Challenge

Finding a good revision routine is difficult, and your child will need to do preparation on top of training tests. This schedule slowly increases the amount of daily work done on three preparatory activities: mental maths, spelling and book reading.

Monday	Tuesday	Wednesday	Thursday	Friday	Saturday	Sunday
Day 1 Mental Maths: *10 Minutes*	Day 2 Spelling Work: *10 Minutes*	Day 3 Read a Book: *10 Minutes*	Day 4 Break: *Full Evening*	Day 5 Mental Maths: *15 Minutes*	Day 6 Spelling Work: *15 Minutes*	Day 7 Read a Book: *15 Minutes*
Day 8 Break: *Full Evening*	Day 9 Mental Maths: *20 Minutes*	Day 10 Spelling Work: *20 Minutes*	Day 11 Read a Book: *20 Minutes*	Day 12 Break: *Full Evening*	Day 13 Mental Maths: *30 Minutes*	Day 14 Spelling Work: *30 Minutes*
Day 15 Read a Book: *30 Minutes*	Day 16 Break: *Full Evening*	Day 17 Mental Maths: *35 Minutes*	Day 18 Spelling Work: *35 Minutes*	Day 19 Read a Book: *35 Minutes*	Day 20 Break: *Full Evening*	Day 21 Mental Maths: *40 Minutes*
Day 22 Spelling Work: *40 Minutes*	Day 23 Read a Book: *40 Minutes*	Day 24 Break: *Full Evening*	Day 25 Mental Maths: *45 Minutes*	Day 26 Spelling Work: *45 Minutes*	Day 27 Read a Book: *45 Minutes*	Day 28 Break: *Full Evening*
Day 29 Mental Maths: *50 Minutes*	Day 30 Spelling Work: *50 Minutes*	Day 31 Read a Book: *50 Minutes*				

In the Run-Up: Intense Learning

It is crucial that your child does not experience burn-out, however in the final weeks their preparation will increase. They should never sit more than two tests in a day, and our routine demonstrates the healthy way to handle the final stretch.

Time:	Monday	Tuesday	Wednesday	Thursday	Friday	Saturday	Sunday
8:00am - 9:00am	Wake up, eat breakfast, and get ready for the day!						
9:00am - 10:00am	Maths - Test 1: *60 Minutes*	VR - Test 1: *40 Minutes*	English - Test 2: *70 Minutes*	NVR - Test 2: *60 Minutes*	Maths - Test 3: *60 Minutes*	VR - Test 3: *40 Minutes*	NVR - Test 3: *60 Minutes*
10:00am - 11:00am	Read a Book	Break: Have a snack (some fruit)		Spelling Work	Break: Watch TV or play games		Mental Maths Work
11:00am - 12:00pm	Maths Review: *25 Minutes*	VR Review: *25 Minutes*	English Review: *25 Minutes*	NVR Review: *25 Minutes*	Maths Review: *25 Minutes*	VR Review: *25 Minutes*	NVR Review: *25 Minutes*
12:00pm - 1:00pm	Lunch Break						
1:00pm - 2:00pm	English - Test 1: *70 Minutes*	NVR - Test 1: *60 Minutes*	Maths - Test 2: *60 Minutes*	VR - Test 2: *40 Minutes*	English - Test 3: *70 Minutes*	Break: Meet some friends or take part in some extracurricular activity	
2:00pm - 3:00pm	Break: Play outside and be active						
3:00pm - 4:00pm	English Review: *25 Minutes*	NVR Review: *25 Minutes*	Maths Review: *25 Minutes*	VR Review: *25 Minutes*	English Review: *25 Minutes*		

Holiday Revision: Blank Timetable

It goes without saying that you know your child best, and so you may wish to create your own custom timetable for your child to work through. The working hours are limited to between 8am and 4pm, as your child is used to school hours.

Time:	Monday	Tuesday	Wednesday	Thursday	Friday	Saturday	Sunday
8:00am - 9:00am							
9:00am - 10:00am							
10:00am - 11:00am							
11:00am - 12:00pm							
12:00pm - 1:00pm							
1:00pm - 2:00pm							
2:00pm - 3:00pm							
3:00pm - 4:00pm							

Advice on Using our Timetables

As much as we want to steer you in the right direction, we at Secondary Entrance acknowledge that every child is unique, and has their own, independent learning style. In accordance with this, we strongly encourage you to modify and adjust our timetables around your child's subject needs, extra-curricular activities and their social life.

That's the end of the book. What else do we offer?

We've got a three part education system, designed to get your child into their chosen school:

1

11+ Practice Papers

240 outstanding quality tests for the 4 core subjects. We've scrutinised every question to ensure quality.

2

Tutoring Services

We offer in-person and online tutoring services. All of our tutors have attended world-leading universities.

3

11+ Practice Papers

www.Independent11Plus.co.uk We provide learning guides and supplementary material.

Meet our authors and editors
For English book 1 to book 4

Our authors have all attended Cambridge and Imperial – world-leading universities.

AUTHOR:
Simon Thackray

MBBS: Imperial
BSc: Imperial
Studying: Medicine

AUTHOR:
Haaris Rahim

MBBS: Imperial
BSc: Imperial
Studying: Medicine

AUTHOR:
Leah Holm-Mercer

MBBS: Imperial
BA: Cambridge
Studying: Medicine

AUTHOR & EDITOR:
Aneesh Aggarwal

MBBS: Cambridge
BA: Cambridge
Studying: Medicine

EDITOR:
Suraj Joshi

MBBS: Imperial
BSc: Imperial
Studying: Medicine

EDITOR:
Christiana Naziris

MSc: Cambridge
BA: Cambridge
Studied: Physics

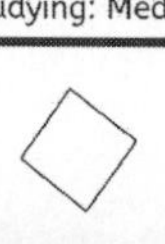

References
Icons from www.flaticon.com

'Tree' icon made by Smashicons
'Books' icon made by Freepik
'Ping Pong' icon made by Freepik
'Apple' icon made by Freepik
'Landscape' icon made by Freepik
'Skipping Rope' icon made by Freepik
'Sleep' icon made by Freepik
'Museum' icon made by Freepik
'Grocery' icon made by Smashicons
'Sunbed' icon made by Smashicons
'Newspaper' icon made by Smashicons
'Backgammon' icon made by Nikita Golubev
'Baby' icon made by Freepik
'Calendar' icon made by Freepik
'Day and Night' icon made by Freepik
'Settings' icon made by Freepik
'Newton's Cradle' icon made by Freepik
'Time' icon made by Freepik
'Bar Chart' icon made by Freepik
'Goal' icon made by Freepik
'Time Management' icon made by Freepik
'Analytics' icon made by Freepik
All other graphics are either open source or produced by Secondary Entrance

Printed in Great Britain
by Amazon